Lesson Assessment Book 1

Level 5

Annotated Teacher's Edition

SRA

A Division of The *McGraw-Hill* Companies

SRAonline.com

 SRA

Send all inquiries to this address:
SRA/McGraw-Hill
4400 Easton Commons
Columbus, OH 43219-6188

ISBN: 978-0-07-613226-3
MHID: 0-07-613226-9

2 3 4 5 6 7 8 9   MAZ   13 12 11 10 09 08

The *McGraw-Hill* Companies

Table of Contents

Imagine It! Lesson Assessment Books

Lesson Assessment Book 1 and *Lesson Assessment Book 2* are an integral part of a complete assessment program that aligns with the instruction in *Imagine It! Lesson Assessment Book 1* covers material from Units 1–3. *Lesson Assessment Book 2* covers material from Units 4–6. The skills featured in lesson assessments are tied to reading success and reflect both state and national standards.

Lesson Assessment Book 1 and *Lesson Assessment Book 2* offer the opportunity for summative and formative assessment. As students complete each lesson, they will be assessed on their understanding of the instructional content and the literature in each lesson. The results of the assessments will then be used to inform subsequent instruction. How students score on the assessments offers a picture of current student achievement status while also guiding you toward appropriate instructional decisions.

Each lesson assessment offers you the ability to gauge students' understanding of and growth in the following areas:

- Vocabulary
- Comprehension
- Grammar, Usage, and Mechanics
- Oral Fluency
- Writing

Lesson Assessments

The lesson assessments consist of the following:

Lesson Area	Format	Scope	Scoring
Vocabulary	Multiple Choice	Selection Vocabulary and Word Structure elements	10 points (5 questions x 2 point)
Comprehension	Multiple Choice	Comprehension Skills	5 points (5 questions x 1 point)
	Short Answer	Comprehension Skills	10 points (5 questions x 2 points)
	Linking to the Concepts (Short Answer)	General comprehension related to a selection	4 points (0-4 rubrics)
	Personal Response (Short Answer)	General comprehension related to a selection	3 points (0-3 rubrics)
	Analyzing the Selection (Extended Response)	Understanding and development of ideas about selections and the unit theme	8 points (0-8 rubrics)
Grammar, Usage, and Mechanics	Multiple Choice	Grammar, Usage, and Mechanics skills practiced in the lesson	10 points (5 questions x 2 point)
Oral Fluency	Teacher-Directed Student Performance	Oral fluency development from lesson to lesson	Accuracy Rate on 100-point scale

Students will be graded on their understanding of the vocabulary, word structure, comprehension, and grammar, usage, and mechanics skills taught in the lesson on a 50-point scale. A score of 80% (or 40 points out of 50) or higher on each lesson assessment is expected. Students may look back at the selection to answer the assessment questions. Students who consistently fall below 80% should be monitored for possible intervention. Students who are consistent low-performers in one or more aspects of the lesson assessment should be offered more practice in this lesson area during Workshop.

The Oral Fluency Assessments are scored separately. These assessments offer further data on student abilities. Student performance on oral fluency assessments is often a reliable predictor of student growth and understanding in other lesson areas. Students with consistently low accuracy rates and below-level words per minute numbers should be provided extra fluency practice during Workshop.

End of Unit Writing Prompt

Over the course of the year, students will encounter six writing prompts, two each in the narrative, expository, and persuasive genres. These prompts reflect students' prior knowledge and experience with writing to a specific genre. Each prompt consists of a writing situation, a specific audience, directions for writing, and a checklist students can reference to ensure they receive the best score possible. Rubrics for scoring student work follow each prompt in this book. These rubrics pertain to genre, writing traits, and conventions. Students will be graded on a 20-point scale based on the rubrics—four points multiplied by five key writing features.

A score of 75% (or 15 points out of 20) or higher on each writing prompt is expected. Students can respond to the prompts in their student workbooks.

Scores and Records

The opening page of each lesson assessment includes a place for students to write their names and the date, and for you to list their scores.

The Oral Fluency Assessment includes a box in which to write the accuracy rate.

The writing prompt includes a place for students to write their names and the date, and for you to list their scores.

Students' scores in the assessment can be registered in the Oral Fluency Scores, Class Assessment Record, and Student Assessment Record pages.

Lesson Assessment Sections

Students may look back at the selection to answer the assessment questions.

Vocabulary

Each vocabulary assessment is comprised of five multiple-choice questions worth two points each. Four of the questions feature selection vocabulary words from the lesson students have just completed. The remaining question in the assessment pertains to a word structure element from that lesson. The format of this question varies based on the word structure feature that is being assessed.

Comprehension: Multiple Choice

Each comprehension assessment begins with five multiple-choice questions worth one point each. The items reflect the comprehension skills students have been taught specifically in that lesson and skills students have been previously taught.

Comprehension: Short Answer

Next, students answer five short-answer questions worth two points each. These questions also reflect comprehension skills specific to the lesson and to students' prior knowledge and understanding of comprehension skills. Well-crafted and concise responses that answer the question fully should be awarded two points. Answers that partially address the question or are confusing and incomplete should be awarded a point, at your discretion. Answers that do not attempt to address the question or provide incorrect information should receive zero points.

Please note the "Possible answers below" following the directions in this Teacher's Edition. This serves as a reminder that students do not have to provide the exact answer shown, and that in some cases more than one answer is possible. For example, questions that ask for "one reason" or "one example" of something might be answered by a reason or example not specified in this Teacher's Edition.

Comprehension: Linking to the Concepts

In this section, students craft a response to a question related to the selection they have just read. These questions do not focus on a particular comprehension skill; rather, they assess general comprehension of a selection by focusing on a key element in a selection which students should be comfortable identifying and writing to or about. These questions are worth four points each. Use the following criteria to judge student responses. To fully answer the question or prompt, student answers should be approximately forty to seventy words.

Score: 4

The student understands the question and responds using information from the selection. The response is correct, reflects a thorough comprehension of the selection, and is an acceptably complete answer to the question. The organization of the response is meaningful, it is written smoothly, and sentences flow together. The response focuses on the topic. If multiple paragraphs are written, they are linked to one another with effective transitions. The response reads easily and demonstrates a sense of audience. It has correct spelling, grammar, usage, and mechanics, and it is written neatly and legibly.

Score: 3

The student understands the question and responds using information from the selection. The response may reflect comprehension of the selection and is a somewhat complete answer to the question. The organization of the response is meaningful, it is written smoothly, and sentences flow together. The response focuses on the topic. If multiple paragraphs are written, they are linked to one another with effective transitions. The response reads easily and demonstrates a sense of audience. It has occasional errors in spelling, grammar, usage, and mechanics, and it is mostly written neatly and legibly.

Score: 2

The student has partial understanding of the question. The response may reflect limited comprehension of the selection and is an incomplete answer to the question. The organization of the response is weak, it is written carelessly, and sentences are somewhat disorganized. The response includes extraneous information. If multiple paragraphs are written, they are linked to one another ineffectively. The response requires some effort to read easily and demonstrates a poor sense of audience. It has occasional errors in spelling, grammar, usage, and mechanics, and it is written somewhat neatly and legibly.

Score: 1

The student has minimal understanding of the question. The response may reflect poor comprehension of the selection and is a barely acceptable answer to the question. The organization of the response is imprecise, it is written erratically, and sentences may be disjointed. The response is poorly focused. If multiple paragraphs are written, they are linked to one another inconsistently. The response is difficult to follow and may cause the reader to struggle. It has frequent errors in spelling, grammar, usage, and mechanics, and it is written with borderline neatness and legibility.

Score: 0

The student fails to compose a response. If a response is attempted, it is inaccurate, meaningless, or irrelevant. The response may be written so poorly that it is neither legible nor understandable.

SAMPLE

The following is an example of a response that would receive a score of "3" if it were mostly written neatly and legibly. The student shows an understanding of the question and relates information pertaining to the selection. The answer is organized, and the sections of the response relate to one another. However, the lack of an example for current wind use and the errors in spelling and grammar prevent it from being an exemplary response.

Linking to the Concepts *How has wind been valuable to people throughout history?*

> *People have used wind for a long time. The first way to use wind was probably a boat. These were made a long time ago. Windmills came next. Windmills were used to create power for businesses. They still use windmills in some places; popepl continue to use wind everyday.*

Comprehension: Personal Response

In this section, students are asked to craft a personal response related to an idea or thematic issue raised by the selection they have just read. This section judges students' level of comprehension by assessing their ability to connect what they have just read to a personal level.

These questions are worth three points each. Use the following criteria to judge student responses. To fully answer the question or prompt, student answers should be approximately forty to seventy words.

Score: 3

The student understands the question and responds suitably using a personal experience, opinion, prior knowledge, or plausible conjecture. The response reflects a thorough comprehension of the selection and is an acceptably complete answer to the question. The organization of the response is meaningful, it is written smoothly, and sentences flow together. The response focuses on the topic. If multiple paragraphs are written, they are linked to one another with effective transitions. The response reads easily and demonstrates a sense of audience. It has correct spelling, grammar, usage, and mechanics, and it is written neatly and legibly.

Score: 2

The student understands the question and responds using a personal experience, opinion, prior knowledge, or plausible conjecture. The response may reflect partial comprehension of the selection and is a somewhat complete answer to the question. The organization of the response is imprecise, it is written erratically, and sentences may be somewhat disjointed. The response is not clearly focused. If multiple paragraphs are written, they are linked to one another ineffectively. The response is difficult to follow and demonstrates little awareness of the reader. It has a moderate number of errors in spelling, grammar, usage, and mechanics, and it is mostly written neatly and legibly.

Score: 1

The student has minimal understanding of the question and responds using a personal experience, opinion, prior knowledge, or plausible conjecture. The response may reflect poor comprehension of the selection and is a barely acceptable answer to the question. The organization of the response is imprecise, it is written erratically, and sentences may be disjointed. The response is poorly focused. If multiple paragraphs are written, they are linked to one another inconsistently. The response is difficult to follow and may cause the reader to struggle. It has frequent errors in spelling, grammar, usage, and mechanics, and it is written with borderline neatness and legibility.

Score: 0

The student fails to compose a response. If a response is attempted, it is inaccurate, meaningless, or irrelevant. The response may be written so poorly that it is neither legible nor understandable.

The following is an example of a response that would receive a score of "2" if it were mostly written neatly and legibly. The student shows an understanding of the question and connects it to plausible, real-world situations. However, the details about the shirts and the time it took to finish the walk are unnecessary, and there are errors in grammar. These facts prevent it from being an exemplary response.

SAMPLE

Personal Response *Think about what Paul Revere did. Write about something you did that was part of a bigger event involving other people.*

> *My mother and I tried to do something important like Revere. We went for a walk to support a cure for cancer. It was a huge event. We paid money and got shirts. We wore our shirts on the walk. The walk took a long time almost an hour. Some of the people ran and we all hoped that what we did would help find a cure.*

Grammar, Usage, and Mechanics

Each grammar, usage, and mechanics assessment is comprised of five multiple-choice questions worth two points each. Each question specifically relates to the lesson material for that week. Students sometimes will be asked to identify errors or incorrect constructions, so remind students to read each question carefully.

Comprehension: Analyzing the Selection

This section of the assessment allows students to craft a longer, more detailed response to show their comprehension of what they have read. It also provides additional data on the writing skills of students as they progress through the program.

Students will sometimes be asked to respond by connecting the selection they have just read to previous selections in the unit.

These questions and prompts are worth eight points each. Use the following criteria to judge student responses. To fully answer the question or prompt, student answers should be approximately one hundred to one hundred and sixty words.

Note: You will notice that the rubrics below each have a two-point range. Use your professional judgment in awarding the higher point total in the scale to students' work.

Score: 8 or 7

The student understands the question and responds suitably using the appropriate source of information. These sources include the selection itself, other selections, personal experience, opinion, prior knowledge, or plausible conjecture. The response reflects a thorough comprehension of the selection and is an acceptably complete answer to the question. The organization of the response is meaningful, it is written smoothly, and both sentences and paragraphs flow together. Paragraphs focus on related topics and are linked to one another with effective transitions. The response reads easily and demonstrates a sense of audience. It has correct spelling, grammar, usage, and mechanics, and it is written neatly and legibly.

Score: 6 or 5

The student understands the question and responds suitably using the appropriate source of information. These sources include the selection itself, other selections, personal experience, opinion, prior knowledge, or plausible conjecture. The response may reflect comprehension of the selection or other sources and is a somewhat complete answer to the question. The organization of the response is somewhat meaningful, and both sentences and paragraphs flow together relatively smoothly. Paragraphs focus on related topics and are linked to one another with effective transitions. The response reads easily and demonstrates a sense of audience. It has occasional errors in spelling, grammar, usage, and mechanics, and it is written somewhat neatly and legibly.

Score: 4 or 3

The student has partial understanding of the question. The response may reflect limited comprehension of the selection and is an incomplete answer to the question or includes irrelevant information. The organization of the response is weak, it is written carelessly, and both sentences and paragraphs are somewhat disorganized. Paragraphs include some extraneous information and are linked to one another ineffectively. The response requires some effort to read easily and demonstrates a poor sense of audience. It has occasional errors in spelling, grammar, usage, and mechanics, and it is written somewhat neatly and legibly.

Score: 2 or 1

The student has minimal understanding of the question. The response may reflect poor comprehension of the selection and is a barely acceptable answer to the question or includes irrelevant information. The organization of the response is imprecise, it is written erratically, and sentences or paragraphs may be disjointed. Paragraphs may be poorly focused or are linked to one another inconsistently. The response is difficult to follow and may cause the reader to struggle. It has frequent errors in spelling, grammar, usage, and mechanics, and it is written with borderline neatness and legibility.

Score: 0

The student fails to compose a response. If a response is attempted, it is inaccurate, meaningless, or irrelevant. The response may be written so poorly that it is neither legible nor understandable.

The following is an example of a response that would receive a score of "4" if written somewhat neatly and legibly. The student shows a partial understanding of the question through the use of examples from the selections. The student makes occasional errors in spelling and grammar. However, the chief concern is that the theme the student identifies—how different people made the West—is not supported by the examples from the selections. This makes the response disorganized and less than convincing.

SAMPLE

Analyzing the Selection *Think about the three selections you have read in this unit. What are some common themes among them? What do these themes tell about the American West?*

One was about buffalo and how Native Americans hunted them. They used the buffalo for everything. They ate the meat and used the skin. When the buffalo were gone the people had a hard time. They probably didn't think the buffalo would ever disappear.

The story about Uncle and Wong was intresting. They were pretty smart. They found gold that other people didn't know about. They pretended to be poor so no one would take their gold.

The rodeo story was about a cowboy who was a rodeo rider. People liked to watch him because he did neat things. He traveled all over the world.

The idea that was the same in all the stories is that different people helped to make the west. These three stories were mostly about people you don't see on television or in the movies. Native Americans, Chinese people, and an African American cowboy.

Oral Fluency Assessments

Administering Oral Fluency Assessments

The Oral Fluency Assessment is an efficient means for evaluating students' ability to read. It is simple to administer and score, yet it provides extraordinarily useful quantitative and qualitative data. You will find oral fluency assessments for each lesson. The words in the selections are of sufficient variety to allow for an analysis of the decoding and vocabulary abilities of a student and to draw inferences about a student's ability to derive meaning from the text.

Make a copy of the Oral Fluency Assessment for each student you will be assessing. Have students turn to the corresponding page in their workbooks. Be sure you have a pen or pencil, a stopwatch or other timer, and extra paper to record any observations. Briefly review the text before you begin. On the Oral Fluency Scores pages, you will record the student's name, the date of the assessment, and the results of the assessment.

Have the student sit comfortably at a table with you. Seat yourself and the student so that you can mark the assessment unobtrusively without distracting the student.

Say: *Here is a selection I would like you to read aloud for me. I am going to listen to you read and take some notes. The notes I take will help me learn how well you can read. You will not be graded for this, so you should not feel nervous. Read the selection carefully and do your best. Take a few minutes now to look over the selection, and then I will tell you when to begin.*

Allow time for the student to preview the story. Be sure you have a pen or pencil.

Say: *Are you ready?* (Check to be sure the student is ready.) *You may begin now.*

Start the timer or watch as the student begins to read. You may pronounce any proper nouns with which the student is unfamiliar. Do not count these words as errors.

Note: If the student becomes frustrated or makes several consecutive errors, stop the assessment.

At the end of one minute place a bracket ( ]) at the end of the last word the student reads.

Scoring Oral Fluency Assessments

The following guidelines will help you score the assessment accurately and consistently.

- Self-correcting should not be counted as an error.
- Repeating the same mistake should be counted as only one error.
- Hesitating for more than five seconds—at which point you would have provided the word—should count as an error.
- Become familiar with the evaluating codes before administering the Oral Fluency Assessment.

Scoring Conventions

- Draw a line through any word that is misread. Count this as an error. If possible, note the type of error. (Misreading *short a* as *short e*, reading *get* as *jet*, and so on).
- Draw a bracket ( ]) at the end of the last word the student reads in one minute.
- Words the student omits should be counted as errors, even if you prompt the student.
- Indicate with a caret extra words that have been inserted. If possible, write the inserted word. Count insertions as errors.
- Draw an arrow between words that have been reversed. Count these as one error.
- Students might repeat words on occasion. Do not count this behavior as an error.

Finding the Student's Accuracy Rate

To find a student's accuracy rate, count the total number of words read in one minute. The numbers beside the passage on the teacher's page will make this an easier task. Subtract the number of errors from the total number of words read and use that figure to find the number of correct words read per minute. Then divide the correct words per minute by the total number of words read to find the accuracy rate. Record these numbers on the Reading Rate and Accuracy chart located on your Oral Fluency Assessment pages.

- Record the student's score on the Oral Fluency Scores pages and the Student Assessment Record.
- Complete the Reading Fluency scale at the bottom of your Oral Fluency Assessment page. These qualitative measures indicate your subjective judgment of how the student compares with other students who are reading at grade level.

READING RATE AND ACCURACY

Total Words Read:	147
Number of Errors:	22
Number of Correct Words Read Per Minute (WPM):	125
Accuracy Rate:	85%

(Number of Correct Words Read per Minute ÷ Total Words Read)

READING FLUENCY

	Low	Average	High
Decoding ability	○	○	●
Pace	○	●	○
Syntax	○	●	○
Self-correction	○	●	○
Intonation	○	○	●

Interpreting the Oral Fluency Assessments

First, compare the student's number of correct words per minute with the following chart. This will give you an idea of how the student compares with other students in the same grade at the same time of year. The data in this chart represents the approximate number of correct words read per minute a student should be reading in Grades 2–6. The two rows of numbers represent the 50th and 75th percentiles.

	Units 1-2	Units 3-4	Units 5-6	
Grade 2	79	100	117	75th Percentile
	51	72	89	50th Percentile
Grade 3	99	120	137	75th Percentile
	71	92	107	50th Percentile
Grade 4	119	139	152	75th Percentile
	94	112	123	50th Percentile
Grade 5	139	156	168	75th Percentile
	110	127	139	50th Percentile
Grade 6	153	167	177	75th Percentile
	127	140	150	50th Percentile

Source Adapted from Hasbrouck, J., & Tindal, G. (2005). Oral Reading Fluency: 90 Years of Measurement (Tech. Rep. No. 33). Eugene, Oregon: University of Oregon, College of Education, Behavioral Research and Teaching.

Then examine the student's accuracy rate. Reading accuracy should remain constant or gradually increase within a grade and between grades, until it stabilizes at ninety percent or higher. You may find it helpful to compare a student's accuracy rate after each administration to ensure that it remains constant or increases.

Next, examine the types of errors the student is making and consider how they represent underlying student behaviors. Here are some examples:

- Inserting extra words suggests that the student understands what is read, is constructing meaning, but is reading somewhat impulsively.

- A student who refuses to attempt to read a word is probably uncertain of his or her abilities and is unwilling to take risks.

- Misreading regular letter sounds implies that the student has not yet mastered the conventions of the sound-symbol relationship. This is in contrast with the student who misreads complex letter sounds (alternate sounds, blends, diphthongs, digraphs, and so on) but has little difficulty with regular letter sounds.

Finally, consider the error pattern. If errors are scattered randomly throughout the passage, then the error types represent skills the student has not yet developed. If errors increase in frequency from beginning to end, then fatigue or inattention likely are involved.

Other Considerations

Several strategies are available for promoting reading fluency and accuracy. These involve pairing an accomplished reader with a developing reader, small-group choral reading, and repeated readings of familiar text.

You may find it useful to establish targets for reading accuracy. These targets may include goals such as reading ten words in a row without error, increasing by increments the number of correct words a student reads in a minute, or decreasing a specific error type. Establishing such targets allows you to provide appropriate instructional support and gives students a reasonable goal.

End of Unit Writing Prompt

The writing prompt offers the opportunity for an on-demand writing performance similar to the type students will encounter in high-stakes testing. Use the rubrics that follow the prompts to judge students' work. Student writing should be included in each student's Writing Portfolio.

Teacher Records

This Teacher's Edition contains record keeping material that will help you keep track of student progress in lesson assessments.

Six Point Rubrics

Six Point Writing Rubrics for assessing student writing are included.

These can take the place of the four point rubrics if you are in a school that uses the six point rubric system.

Oral Fluency Scores

These pages allow you to note student accuracy rates throughout the year.

Class Assessment Record

These pages offer a warehouse for class scores.

The spaces following the student's name allow for the recording of student scores in each lesson assessment (out of the 50-point scale) and each writing prompt (using the four point or six point rubrics to assess).

The format of the Class Assessment Record provides an easy way to monitor student growth across the year.

Student Assessment Record

You can duplicate this page for each student and use it to track student progress.

Comprehension Observation Log

Observing students as they read anthology selections is an effective way to learn their strengths and areas of need in comprehension. Use the Comprehension Observation Log to record your observations of students. Choose a small set of students to focus on for a particular lesson. You might want to observe students more than once to get a clear idea of their comprehension of texts. Copy this page for each student or group of students you observe.

Name _____ Date _____ Score _____

The Land I Lost

Vocabulary

Read each item. Fill in the bubble for the answer you think is correct.

1. What does the Latin root *spir* mean?

Ⓐ book   Ⓒ breath

Ⓑ band   Ⓓ ball

2. Lingered means about the same as

Ⓐ watched.   Ⓒ danced.

Ⓑ stayed.   Ⓓ wished.

3. People **assumed** the grandfather knew karate. **Assumed** means

Ⓐ helped someone do something.

Ⓑ said something nice about someone.

Ⓒ wondered if something were true.

Ⓓ believed something without proof.

4. According to the grandmother's **logic,** there would be bad luck next year. **Logic** has to do with

Ⓐ the way you think.

Ⓑ the way you treat others.

Ⓒ how old you are.

Ⓓ how much you like music.

5. The grandmother's plays were **inspired** by books. Being **inspired** by something means that it

Ⓐ made you famous.   Ⓒ gave you an idea.

Ⓑ had to be kept secret.   Ⓓ was unlike anything else.

The Land I Lost (continued)

Comprehension

Read the following questions carefully. Then completely fill in the bubble of each correct answer. You may look back at the selection to find the answer to each of the questions.

1. What is the first part of the selection mainly about?
   - Ⓐ the hunting trips in the jungle
   - Ⓑ the grandmother and grandfather
   - Ⓒ the experience of seeing an opera
   - Ⓓ the place where the narrator once lived

2. The narrator of this selection is
   - Ⓐ a man who remembers his boyhood.
   - Ⓑ a grandmother who loves opera.
   - Ⓒ a grandfather who is very shy.
   - Ⓓ a father who is raising a family.

The Land I Lost (continued)

3. Why did the homes in the hamlet have deep trenches around them?

Ⓐ to protect their rice plants

Ⓑ to prevent water from flooding in

Ⓒ to keep out thieves and wild animals

Ⓓ to keep the children from wandering off

4. The author wrote this selection in order to

Ⓐ persuade readers to visit Vietnam.

Ⓑ tell readers about his family and life in Vietnam.

Ⓒ give a short history of Vietnam.

Ⓓ share a funny folktale from Vietnam.

5. Which of these was the most feared in the hamlet?

Ⓐ a man-eating tiger

Ⓑ a lone wild hog

Ⓒ a horse snake

Ⓓ a swamp crocodile

The Land I Lost (continued)

Read the following questions carefully. Use complete sentences to answer the questions. Possible answers below

6. How is the narrator's grandfather different from his grandmother?

He is shy, quiet, and not strong. The grandmother is loud and strong.

7. Why did people treat the grandfather with respect?

They thought he was good at karate.

8. Why does the grandmother sigh when she first sees the "Faithful One" onstage?

She sighs because she thinks this means bad fortune for the year.

9. What are some clues that the grandmother is preparing to die at the end of the story?

She wants to visit the graveyard; she says "Dear, I will join you soon," to the grandfather's tombstone.

10. Why is this selection called "The Land I Lost"?

The narrator's boyhood home is "lost" when he goes away to study.

The Land I Lost (continued)

Read the question below. Write complete sentences for your answer. Support your answer with information from the selection.

Linking to the Concepts What do the stories reveal about the type of person the grandmother was?

_____

_____

_____

_____

_____

Read the question below. Your answer should be based on your own experience. Write complete sentences for your answer.

Personal Response How would you describe where you live to the narrator of this selection?

_____

_____

_____

_____

_____

The Land I Lost (continued)

Grammar, Usage, and Mechanics

Read each question. Fill in the bubble beside the answer in each group that is correct. If none of the answers is correct, choose the last answer, "none of the above."

1. In which sentence is a noun underlined?

   Ⓐ The zebra <u>drank</u> slowly. Ⓒ The zebra drank <u>slowly</u>.

   Ⓑ The <u>zebra</u> drank slowly. Ⓓ none of the above

2. In which sentence is a proper noun underlined?

   Ⓐ Uncle Ned <u>went</u> on a safari to Africa.

   Ⓑ Uncle Ned went on a <u>safari</u> to Africa.

   Ⓒ Uncle Ned went on a safari to <u>Africa</u>.

   Ⓓ none of the above

3. In which sentence is the direct object underlined?

   Ⓐ The lion chased a <u>zebra</u> through the tall grass.

   Ⓑ The lion chased a zebra <u>through</u> the tall grass.

   Ⓒ The lion chased a zebra through the <u>tall</u> grass.

   Ⓓ none of the above

4. In which sentence is an action verb underlined?

   Ⓐ The zebra <u>seemed</u> to be tiring.

   Ⓑ The lion <u>pounced</u>, but missed the zebra.

   Ⓒ The zebra <u>had</u> a chance to get away.

   Ⓓ none of the above

5. In which sentence is a linking verb underlined?

   Ⓐ The lion <u>turned</u> to look for another zebra.

   Ⓑ The zebras by the pond <u>became</u> very scared.

   Ⓒ They bounded <u>across</u> the plains.

   Ⓓ none of the above

The Land I Lost (continued)

Analyzing the Selection

Read the questions below. Write complete sentences for your answer. Support your answer with information from the selection.

Why do you think the author remembers the particular incidents described in the "The Land I Lost"? Why are certain family events in your life so easy to remember?

_____

_____

_____

_____

_____

_____

_____

_____

_____

_____

_____

_____

The Land I Lost (continued)

Oral Fluency Assessment

Tim Sees Saturn

Tim and his mother joined the group going into the building.   1–11
Tim was still a little confused about the surprise his mother   12–22
mentioned, but he was also curious. The inside of the building   23–33
was a huge dome. In the middle was a strange-looking device.   34–45

"This is a sixty-inch telescope," Dr. Miller told the group.   46–56
"By looking through it we can view stars and planets close up."   57–68
She explained that tonight they would be looking at the planet   69–79
Saturn, as well as other objects in the night sky. "Why don't you   80–92
go first, Tim?"   93–95

He hesitated for a minute because everyone was watching   96–104
him. Finally, he put his face closer to the eyepiece. He looked   105–116
through it with one eye and closed the other one. Through   117–127
the telescope Tim saw a big, round, glowing planet with rings   128–138
around it. Tim had seen Saturn before, but it was just a tiny   139–151
light in the night sky. Now, it was many times bigger, and the   152–164
rings were beautiful. "Wow! It looks so different through the   165–174
telescope!" he exclaimed.   175–177

"Well," asked Mrs. Barker, holding her son's shoulders, "now   178–186
would you rather we went home to watch the big game?"   187–197

"Forget the game," Tim replied. "This is great."   198–205

**EVALUATING CODES
FOR ORAL FLUENCY**

sky   (/) words read incorrectly

blue
  ^ sky   (^) inserted word
           ( ]) after the last word

READING RATE AND ACCURACY

Total Words Read: _____

Number of Errors: _____

Number of Correct Words
Read Per Minute (WPM):   _____

Accuracy Rate: _____

(Number of Correct Words Read per
Minute ÷ Total Words Read)

READING FLUENCY

	Low	Average	High
Decoding ability	O	O	O
Pace	O	O	O
Syntax	O	O	O
Self-correction	O	O	O
Intonation	O	O	O

Record student rates on the Oral Fluency Scores pages.

Name _____ Date _____ Score _____

Our Song

Vocabulary

Read each item. Fill in the bubble for the answer you think is correct.

1. The prefix **dis-** means

   Ⓐ before.
   Ⓒ too little.

   Ⓑ not.
   Ⓓ across.

2. Another word for **mist** is

   Ⓐ sound.
   Ⓒ land.

   Ⓑ night.
   Ⓓ fog.

3. When Ole Ma was young, she was **delicate. Delicate** means that she was

   Ⓐ loud and rude.
   Ⓒ sad and lonely.

   Ⓑ small and weak.
   Ⓓ quiet and shy.

4. The villagers **ship** peanuts all over the world. In this sentence, **ship** means

   Ⓐ to store something.

   Ⓑ to taste something.

   Ⓒ to plant something.

   Ⓓ to send something.

5. The market in this selection has a lot of **traders. Traders** are people who

   Ⓐ design and build homes.

   Ⓑ travel and put on shows.

   Ⓒ buy and sell goods.

   Ⓓ prepare and cook food.

Our Song (continued)

Comprehension

Read the following questions carefully. Then completely fill in the bubble of each correct answer. You may look back at the selection to find the answer to each of the questions.

1. Which of these makes the narrator like "Our Song" so much?

    Ⓐ It is from another country.

    Ⓑ It is sung by her grandmother.

    Ⓒ It is about a girl from long ago.

    Ⓓ It is in another language.

2. Which of these reminds Ole Ma of her home in Sengal?

    Ⓐ the game of basketball

    Ⓑ the sound of the wind

    Ⓒ the warmth of the sun

    Ⓓ the smells carried by the wind

Our Song (continued)

3. How are Ole Ma and the narrator alike?

   Ⓐ They both enjoy sports.

   Ⓑ They both have big feet.

   Ⓒ They both like lavender.

   Ⓓ They both are good singers.

4. Ole Ma most often sings "Our Song" when

   Ⓐ her granddaughter needs comfort.

   Ⓑ she misses her homeland.

   Ⓒ she has chores to do.

   Ⓓ her feet are being tickled.

5. How was Ole Ma's childhood different from the narrator's?

   Ⓐ She had lots of cousins.

   Ⓑ She played only with girls.

   Ⓒ She grew up in a village.

   Ⓓ She spoke one language.

Our Song (continued)

Read the following questions carefully. Use complete sentences to answer the questions. Possible answers below

6. Why is the narrator so excited to visit Senegal?

She will finally get to see where her grandmother is from.

7. What types of things does the narrator do with her cousins in Senegal?

They show her hiding places and where peanuts are bagged and shipped.

8. How is December in Senegal different from December back home?

It is warm enough to sleep outside and wear shorts without shoes or a hat.

9. What details suggest that Ole Ma is happy to be back in Senegal?

She smiles a lot and talks late into the night with family and friends.

10. Why do the older village women call the narrator Little Goat?

She is always running and jumping around with her cousins.

Our Song (continued)

Read the question below. Write complete sentences for your answer. Support your answer with information from the selection.

Linking to the Concepts How does visiting Senegal change the way the narrator thinks?

_____

_____

_____

_____

_____

_____

Read the question below. Your answer should be based on your own experience. Write complete sentences for your answer.

Personal Response Is there a place that makes you feel especially happy? Describe the place.

_____

_____

_____

_____

_____

_____

Our Song (continued)

Grammar, Usage, and Mechanics

Read each question. Fill in the bubble beside the answer in each group that is correct. If none of the answers is correct, choose the last answer, "none of the above."

1. In which sentence is the subject of the sentence underlined?

Ⓐ Maria <u>decorated</u> the house.

Ⓑ <u>Maria</u> decorated the house.

Ⓒ Maria decorated the <u>house</u>.

Ⓓ none of the above

2. Which of these is a simple sentence?

Ⓐ Next Friday is the start of our vacation.

Ⓑ We cannot go now, but we will meet soon.

Ⓒ After we pack, I will call you.

Ⓓ none of the above

3. Which of these is an interrogative sentence?

Ⓐ Three people forgot to take their coats after the party.

Ⓑ Which of these coats belongs to Jose?

Ⓒ Give that coat to Leon, please.

Ⓓ none of the above

4. Which of these is an imperative sentence?

Ⓐ Mom needs some help in the kitchen making lunch.

Ⓑ What are you doing to help?

Ⓒ Please wash and peel those apples.

Ⓓ none of the above

5. Which of these is an exclamatory sentence?

Ⓐ Tonight is the game.   Ⓒ Hooray, we won!

Ⓑ Are you going?   Ⓓ none of the above

Our Song (continued)

Analyzing the Selection

Read the question below. Write complete sentences for your answer. Support your answer with information from the selection.

What part of the selection is most like an experience you have had? Compare that part of the selection with your experience. Explain how they are alike.

_____

_____

_____

_____

_____

_____

_____

_____

_____

_____

_____

_____

Our Song (continued)

Oral Fluency Assessment

The Family Tree

"We were talking about grandparents in school today," Pam	1–9
said. She sat down by her mother at the kitchen table. "How did	10–22
Grandma and Grandpa meet each other, anyway?"	23–29
"I'm so happy you are interested in your family history,"	30–39
her mother replied, smiling. "Well, all right. They met in 1936	40–50
when they helped out on the same farm after school. Grandma's	51–61
mother and father had just moved to town, and grandma didn't	62–72
have many friends yet."	73–76
Pam was excited, and she asked, "How do you know all of	77–88
this stuff, Mom?"	89–91
"For the past few years, your father and I have been working	92–103
on our family histories," her mother answered. "We have	104–112
studied our families, and we've made a family tree that goes all	113–124
the way back to 1749."	125–129
"What's a family tree?" asked Pam, getting a little confused.	130–139
Pam watched as her mother drew an example of a family	140–150
tree. She followed the lines her mother drew and the names	151–161
she wrote. Then she listened to stories about her family. Some	162–172
were funny. Others were very sad. Pam learned that she had an	173–184
easier life than the people who had come before her.	185–194
"Please tell me more," Pam pleaded.	195–200
Her mother smiled. "That's enough for one night, Pam."	201–209

**EVALUATING CODES
FOR ORAL FLUENCY**

sky   (/) words read incorrectly

blue
^   sky   (^) inserted word
          ( ]) after the last word

READING RATE AND ACCURACY

Total Words Read: _____

Number of Errors: _____

Number of Correct Words
Read Per Minute (WPM): _____

Accuracy Rate: _____

(Number of Correct Words Read per
Minute ÷ Total Words Read)

READING FLUENCY

	Low	Average	High
Decoding ability	○	○	○
Pace	○	○	○
Syntax	○	○	○
Self-correction	○	○	○
Intonation	○	○	○

Record student rates on the Oral Fluency Scores pages.

Name _____ Date _____ Score _____

The Dancing Bird of Paradise

Vocabulary

Read each item. Fill in the bubble for the answer you think is correct.

1. The prefix *en-* in the word *enable* means

   Ⓐ to begin.   Ⓒ to cause to.

   Ⓑ to do again.   Ⓓ to stop.

2. Another word for **startled** is

   Ⓐ surprised.   Ⓒ tired.

   Ⓑ angry.   Ⓓ puzzled.

3. Yuki's **kimono** swished and flared to the music. A **kimono** is

   Ⓐ a type of Japanese dance.

   Ⓑ a Japanese fan made of paper.

   Ⓒ a kind of Japanese robe.

   Ⓓ a Japanese dance teacher.

4. In the story, Sahomi **donned** beautiful costumes. **Donned** means

   Ⓐ wished for.

   Ⓑ studied.

   Ⓒ sewed.

   Ⓓ put on.

5. In New York City, Sahomi sometimes **soloed** as a dancer. **Soloed** means that she

   Ⓐ had a difficult time earning a living.

   Ⓑ performed by herself.

   Ⓒ wished for a different career.

   Ⓓ traveled from place to place.

The Dancing Bird of Paradise (continued)

Comprehension

Read the following questions carefully. Then completely fill in the bubble of each correct answer. You may look back at the selection to find the answer to each of the questions.

1. Why does Haruno change her name?

    (A) She plans to become a dance teacher.

    (B) She is returning to the United States.

    (C) She is honored by her dance school.

    (D) She hears that Japan may go to war.

2. In which of these places did Sahomi begin teaching?

    (A) a farm near San Francisco

    (B) a dance school in Japan

    (C) a dance school in New York City

    (D) a relocation camp in Utah

The Dancing Bird of Paradise (continued)

3. This selection is told from

Ⓐ the second-person point of view.

Ⓑ the third-person point of view.

Ⓒ the first-person point of view.

Ⓓ the point of view of Sahomi.

4. You can tell that news of Sahomi's talent spread because

Ⓐ the wife of the president came to see her dance.

Ⓑ she moved from Pennsylvania to New York.

Ⓒ her costumes shone brighter than before.

Ⓓ the American government realized its mistake.

5. The selection suggests that Sahomi dances mainly to

Ⓐ avoid thinking about the past.

Ⓑ keep her body fit and strong.

Ⓒ share her culture with others.

Ⓓ spread peace among nations.

The Dancing Bird of Paradise (continued)

Read the following questions carefully. Use complete sentences to answer the questions. Possible answers below

6. Why did the children not wear traditional kimonos during their first recital?

   The summer heat was too warm for the children to wear the outfits.

7. What special instructions did Sahomi give her students at the Topaz Relocation Center?

   She told them to dance their best and make the beauty of Japan come alive.

8. How did Sahomi help her young students picture what each dance was about?

   She told them the story and meaning behind each dance.

9. Explain how life was different for Haruno after her cousin Yuki visited her in 1931.

   She found she had a talent for dance and moved to Japan to study dance.

10. What different types of dance did Sahomi study besides Japanese dance?

   She studied ballet and modern dance with the famous Martha Graham.

The Dancing Bird of Paradise (continued)

Read the question below. Write complete sentences for your answer. Support your answer with information from the selection.

Linking to the Concepts What types of things might Sahomi's students say about her?

_____

_____

_____

_____

_____

_____

Read the question below. Your answer should be based on your own experience. Write complete sentences for your answer.

Personal Response If you had students, what important message would you want to teach them? Explain your answer.

_____

_____

_____

_____

_____

_____

The Dancing Bird of Paradise (continued)

Grammar, Usage, and Mechanics

Read each question. Fill in the bubble beside the answer in each group that is correct. If none of the answers is correct, choose the last answer, "none of the above."

1. In which sentence is the adjective underlined?

    Ⓐ The tiny poodle <u>stood</u>.   Ⓒ The tiny <u>poodle</u> stood.

    Ⓑ The <u>tiny</u> poodle stood.   Ⓓ none of the above

2. In which sentence is the adjective used correctly?

    Ⓐ Xavia is the more beautiful town we visited.

    Ⓑ Xavia is the most beautifulest town we visited.

    Ⓒ Xavia is the most beautiful town we visited.

    Ⓓ none of the above

3. Which sentence is a declarative sentence?

    Ⓐ The swimmers raced quickly across the pool.

    Ⓑ Who is in the lead?

    Ⓒ Vida won the meet!

    Ⓓ none of the above

4. In which sentence is the adverb used correctly?

    Ⓐ The crowd cheered loudly for the winner.

    Ⓑ The crowd cheered most loud for the winner.

    Ⓒ The crowd cheered more louder for the winner.

    Ⓓ none of the above

5. In which sentence is the word modified by an adverb underlined?

    Ⓐ The <u>furry</u> hamster raced wildly in his turning wheel.

    Ⓑ The furry hamster raced wildly in his <u>turning</u> wheel.

    Ⓒ The furry hamster raced <u>wildly</u> in his turning wheel.

    Ⓓ none of the above

The Dancing Bird of Paradise (continued)

Analyzing the Selection

Read the question below. Write complete sentences for your answer. Support your answer with information from the selections.

Think about the selections "The Land I Lost," "Our Song," and "The Dancing Bird of Paradise." What do the selections say about the importance of heritage?

_____

_____

_____

_____

_____

_____

_____

_____

_____

_____

_____

_____

_____

_____

The Dancing Bird of Paradise (continued)

Oral Fluency Assessment

A Prized Possession

Dad rose from his seat and walked to Thomas's chair. "Son, I	1–12
have been waiting for your birthday to give you a very special	13–24
gift. My father gave these stamps to me when I was about	25–36
your age. This collection has been one of my most cherished	37–47
possessions, and now I want to give it to you." He placed a	48–60
dusty shoe box in front of Thomas.	61–67
Thomas untied the frayed string and opened the lid of the	68–78
box. Inside he found several yellowed envelopes stuffed full.	79–87
Under the envelopes was a thin book. He opened the book and	88–99
discovered page after page of postage stamps.	100–106
Thomas attempted to appear excited about his gift, but	107–115
he did not understand what was so great about a box of old	116–128
stamps. "Thanks," he said, with a forced smile.	129–136
Then he noticed that Tammy had taken the box. She was	137–147
looking in each envelope. "Look at this one!" she exclaimed.	148–157
"It's from the year I was born. Hey, Thomas, that's the year you	158–170
were born, too!"	171–173
Thomas began to understand why the box was so important	174–183
to his father and grandfather. He moved over by Tammy so	184–194
that he could see the stamps better. Twenty minutes later, he	195–205
did not even notice that his ice cream had melted all over his	206–218
birthday cake.	219–220

READING RATE AND ACCURACY

Total Words Read: _____

Number of Errors: _____

Number of Correct Words
Read Per Minute (WPM): _____

Accuracy Rate: _____

(Number of Correct Words Read per
Minute ÷ Total Words Read)

READING FLUENCY

	Low	Average	High
Decoding ability	○	○	○
Pace	○	○	○
Syntax	○	○	○
Self-correction	○	○	○
Intonation	○	○	○

Record student rates on the Oral Fluency Scores pages.

Name _____ Date _____ Score _____

From Miss Ida's Porch

Vocabulary

Read each item. Fill in the bubble for the answer you think is correct.

1. **Spellbound** means
   - Ⓐ sleepy.
   - Ⓒ doubtful.
   - Ⓑ secretive.
   - Ⓓ fascinated.

2. What is one meaning of the suffix **-ant?**
   - Ⓐ characterized by
   - Ⓒ full of
   - Ⓑ one who does
   - Ⓓ without

3. Daddy attended a **concert** at the Lincoln Memorial. In this sentence, **concert** means
   - Ⓐ a music performance.
   - Ⓒ a storytelling event.
   - Ⓑ a family reunion.
   - Ⓓ a presidential speech.

4. Constitution Hall is called the **forbidden** hall. If a place is **forbidden,** it means
   - Ⓐ you do not know how to get there.
   - Ⓑ special events are held there.
   - Ⓒ history was made there.
   - Ⓓ you are not allowed there.

5. When telling a story, Uncle Henry would **claim** the floor. In this sentence, **claim** means
   - Ⓐ shout something out loud.
   - Ⓑ take something as your own.
   - Ⓒ disagree with something.
   - Ⓓ complain about something.

From Miss Ida's Porch (continued)

Comprehension

Read the following questions carefully. Then completely fill in the bubble of each correct answer. You may look back at the selection to find the answer to each of the questions.

1. Why is Miss Ida's porch special?

Ⓐ It is the nicest porch in the neighborhood.

Ⓑ Neighbors gather there to share stories.

Ⓒ There is always something to eat there.

Ⓓ Famous people used to meet there.

2. Daddy takes a seat on the porch because

Ⓐ Shoo Kate has agreed to tell her story again.

Ⓑ Miss Ida brings a chair just for him.

Ⓒ he wants to tell a tale about Uncle Henry.

Ⓓ he has to keep an eye on his children.

From Miss Ida's Porch (continued)

3. Daddy begins to breathe loud and hard because he is

Ⓐ angry about how African Americans were treated.

Ⓑ tired after walking up Miss Ida's porch steps.

Ⓒ annoyed with how Sylvia is acting.

Ⓓ sad when he remembers Uncle Henry.

4. Which of these stories is told last?

Ⓐ Shoo Kate's story about seeing Marian Anderson.

Ⓑ Uncle Henry's story about the Lincoln Memorial.

Ⓒ Daddy's story about what made Uncle Henry special.

Ⓓ Daddy's story about Marian Anderson's last concert.

5. Which of these is a fact about Uncle Henry, and not an opinion?

Ⓐ He was everyone's favorite.

Ⓑ He was one of the lucky ones.

Ⓒ He was over six feet tall.

Ⓓ He was a grand old guy.

From Miss Ida's Porch (continued)

Read the following questions carefully. Use complete sentences to answer the questions. Possible answers below

6. What are some ways Daddy is like his Uncle Henry?

They both command respect, have deep voices, and are good storytellers.

7. What does the narrator mean when she says, "My dad's story brought the end to the very best time that evening"?

After his story, it was time for the narrator to leave Ida's and go to bed.

8. How can you tell that Daddy's story is "fuel" for the narrator's young mind?

His stories help her picture the past and imagine people and events.

9. According to Uncle Henry, what helps you to know where you are going?

You have to know your history, or where you have been.

10. What does the narrator see and hear just before she drifts off to sleep?

She can see Miss Ida's porch and she can hear the people talking there.

From Miss Ida's Porch (continued)

Read the question below. Write complete sentences for your answer. Support your answer with information from the selection.

Linking to the Concepts How are the people on Ida's porch sharing their history?

_____

_____

_____

_____

_____

Read the question below. Your answer should be based on your own experience. Write complete sentences for your answer.

Personal Response What story might you or another family member tell on Ida's porch? Explain why this story is so important to your family.

_____

_____

_____

_____

_____

From Miss Ida's Porch (continued)

Grammar, Usage, and Mechanics

Read each question. Fill in the bubble beside the answer in each group that is correct. If none of the answers is correct, choose the last answer, "none of the above."

1. Which sentence has correct punctuation?
- Ⓐ Pie, cake, and cookies, are for sale.
- Ⓑ Pie, cake, and cookies are for sale.
- Ⓒ Pie, cake and cookies are for sale.
- Ⓓ none of the above

2. Which sentence has correct punctuation?
- Ⓐ After the, rain the air smelled fresh and clean.
- Ⓑ After the rain the air, smelled fresh and clean.
- Ⓒ After the rain, the air smelled fresh and clean.
- Ⓓ none of the above

3. Which sentence has correct punctuation?
- Ⓐ The band came into town last, and the parade ended.
- Ⓑ The band came into town last and the parade ended.
- Ⓒ The band came into town last and, the parade ended.
- Ⓓ none of the above

4. Which sentence is correct?
- Ⓐ "Practice your scales every day" She said.
- Ⓑ "practice your scales every day", she said.
- Ⓒ "Practice your scales every day," she said.
- Ⓓ none of the above

5. Which item has correct capitalization?
- Ⓐ Akron, Ohio
- Ⓑ akron, ohio
- Ⓒ Akron, ohio
- Ⓓ none of the above

From Miss Ida's Porch (continued)

Analyzing the Selection

Read the questions below. Write complete sentences for your answer. Support your answer with information from the selection.

Why are places like Ida's porch so important to people? Do you think these places have been important to people throughout history?

_____

_____

_____

_____

_____

_____

_____

_____

_____

_____

_____

_____

From Miss Ida's Porch (continued)

Oral Fluency Assessment

Going to Work with Mom

Traci was lucky. Although some of her friends dreaded	1–9
"Take Your Child to Work Day," Traci enjoyed it. Her mother	10–20
worked for the city parks department, so her job often took	21–31
her outdoors.	32–33
This morning the two of them were walking through a	34–43
strip of park that separated the river from the city. Bicyclists	44–54
whizzed past.	55–56
"Here we are," Traci's mother said, pointing to a building up	57–67
ahead. "That's the reason we're here."	68–73
Because the parks department usually dealt with	74–80
landscaping and trails, Traci was puzzled. Her mother	81–88
explained that the building was owned by the city. It had once	89–100
been a restaurant.	101–103
"After the restaurant moved out, we bought the building.	104–112
Our job today is to brainstorm ways to use it," her mother said.	113–125
The two walked around the building. As bikes continued to	126–135
stream past, Traci asked, "We have a lot of bicycle riders in	136–147
town, don't we?"	148–150
"We're one of the nation's leaders," her mother said proudly.	151–160
Traci said, "All those people riding to work downtown might	161–170
need a place to shower and change into their work clothes.	171–181
Could this building be used for that?"	182–188
Her mother nodded, "Maybe it could be a repair shop with	189–199
bicycle storage, too."	200–202
"Great minds think alike, Mom," Traci said. "It's a good thing	203–213
I came with you today!"	214–218

EVALUATING CODES FOR ORAL FLUENCY

sky   (/) words read incorrectly

blue

^ sky   (^) inserted word

( ]) after the last word

READING RATE AND ACCURACY

Total Words Read: _____

Number of Errors: _____

Number of Correct Words
Read Per Minute (WPM): _____

Accuracy Rate: _____

(Number of Correct Words Read per
Minute ÷ Total Words Read)

READING FLUENCY

	Low	Average	High
Decoding ability	○	○	○
Pace	○	○	○
Syntax	○	○	○
Self-correction	○	○	○
Intonation	○	○	○

Record student rates on the Oral Fluency Scores pages.

Name _____ Date _____ Score _____

In Two Worlds

Vocabulary

Read each item. Fill in the bubble for the answer you think is correct.

1. What is one meaning of the suffix **-ence?**

Ⓐ without
Ⓑ full of
Ⓒ wrongly
Ⓓ quality or state

2. Another word for **inhabit** is

Ⓐ live.
Ⓑ understand.
Ⓒ question.
Ⓓ move.

3. The Alaskan tundra is **vast.** If something is **vast,** it is

Ⓐ without human life.
Ⓑ frozen year-round.
Ⓒ very great in size.
Ⓓ in need of protection.

4. The students want to be **fluent** in English and Yup'ik. **Fluent** means

Ⓐ able to speak easily.
Ⓑ able to teach others.
Ⓒ able to write books.
Ⓓ able to visit an area.

5. When the weather grew cold, the plants **withered. Withered** means that the plants

Ⓐ leaned toward the sun.
Ⓑ became dry and wilted.
Ⓒ sent roots down deep.
Ⓓ grew straight and strong.

In Two Worlds (continued)

Comprehension

Read the following questions carefully. Then completely fill in the bubble of each correct answer. You may look back at the selection to find the answer to each of the questions.

1. What does it mean that the Yup'ik Eskimo moved "with the seasons"?

   Ⓐ They had to follow the sun in order to stay warm.

   Ⓑ They grew bored if they stayed in one place too long.

   Ⓒ They went to where food or game was available.

   Ⓓ They traveled only during traditional holidays.

2. What is something Alice does that her mother did not do?

   Ⓐ She bakes bread on a wood stove.

   Ⓑ She has a paying job.

   Ⓒ She spends most evenings telling stories.

   Ⓓ She teaches her girls how to sew.

In Two Worlds (continued)

3. What do the Rivers children have that their parents did not have?

Ⓐ the chance to learn English

Ⓑ the opportunity to go fishing

Ⓒ the chance to attend school

Ⓓ the ability to watch television

4. How is Scammon Bay different today from how it used to be?

Ⓐ It has more contact with the outside world.

Ⓑ It has fewer people living in it.

Ⓒ It has a greater variety of wildlife.

Ⓓ It has one big school instead of many little schools.

5. Which of the Yup'ik traditions has remained with the Rivers family?

Ⓐ living in a home made out of sod

Ⓑ fishing and hunting for food

Ⓒ burning seal oil lamps for light

Ⓓ sitting on the floor while eating

In Two Worlds (continued)

Read the following questions carefully. Use complete sentences to answer the questions. Possible answers below

6. How has the arrival of planes changed life in Scammon Bay?

The planes bring information, goods, and opportunities from the outside.

7. How has education changed over the years in Scammon Bay?

Schools have been built and grown larger, and Yup'ik is now taught.

8. What does the author mean by "Their mark on the land was light"?

The Yup'ik did not change the land very much but left it as it was.

9. How is Billy a teacher to his children?

He teaches them about ice, how to hunt and fish, and how to sit in a boat.

10. What skills do the Rivers think their children need in order to survive in a fast-changing Scammon Bay?

They need to be educated, get good jobs, and learn outside ways.

In Two Worlds (continued)

Read the questions below. Write complete sentences for your answer. Support your answer with information from the selection.

Linking to the Concepts Has life improved in Scammon Bay? Why or why not?

_____

_____

_____

_____

_____

Read the question below. Your answer should be based on your own experience. Write complete sentences for your answer.

Personal Response How is your life different from your parents' and grandparents' childhoods? Give examples of how they are different.

_____

_____

_____

_____

_____

In Two Worlds (continued)

Grammar, Usage, and Mechanics

Read each question. Fill in the bubble beside the answer in each group that is correct. If none of the answers is correct, choose the last answer, "none of the above."

1. In which sentence is a proper noun underlined?

   Ⓐ We took a <u>trip</u> to Florida. Ⓒ We <u>took</u> a trip to Florida.

   Ⓑ We took a trip to <u>Florida</u>. Ⓓ none of the above

2. Which sentence is correct?

   Ⓐ When Aunt Leah arrives, we will begin a long tour of Key West.

   Ⓑ She and Uncle ted is driving from New Jersey.

   Ⓒ They plan to stop brief in north Carolina and Georgia.

   Ⓓ none of the above

3. Which of these is a simple sentence?

   Ⓐ The frog leaped, but the fly got away.

   Ⓑ The big, green frog was hungry and tired.

   Ⓒ After some time had gone by, another fly flew past.

   Ⓓ none of the above

4. Which sentence has a compound predicate?

   Ⓐ The fly buzzed by a second time.

   Ⓑ This surprised the frog, but he flicked out his tongue.

   Ⓒ The frog jumped and splashed into the pond.

   Ⓓ none of the above

5. Which of these is an imperative sentence?

   Ⓐ Give the paper to the student behind you.

   Ⓑ It is my turn to speak!

   Ⓒ Was the man on the left here first?

   Ⓓ none of the above

In Two Worlds (continued)

Analyzing the Selection

Read the question below. Write complete sentences for your answer. Support your answer with information from the selection.

In the selection "In Two Worlds," the Rivers family lives in the same area their family has inhabited for thousands of years. How do you think this affects family traditions?

_____

_____

_____

_____

_____

_____

_____

_____

_____

_____

_____

_____

_____

In Two Worlds (continued)

Oral Fluency Assessment

A Trunk Full of Treasures

Something about closed or locked boxes had always	1–8
intrigued Megan. So when her father pushed a dusty trunk from	9–19
the back of the garage to get at a bicycle that was hung on the	20–34
wall, Megan's eyes lit up.	35–39
"Hey, what's in there?"	40–43
Megan's father turned to her. He wiped his hands on his	44–54
jeans. "I think it has your mother's old high school yearbooks in	55–66
it. Old photos, things like that." He waved his hand.	67–76
Megan's father wiped cobwebs off the bicycle. Megan ran	77–85
over and popped open the trunk's heavy lid. The trunk gave off	86–97
a musty but not unpleasant odor. And, just as Megan's father	98–108
had guessed, it was full of yearbooks, framed pictures, and	109–118
other keepsakes from decades ago.	119–123
In other words, for someone like Megan, it was a treasure	124–134
chest! Megan pulled a yearbook out and leafed through it. She	135–145
kept her eyes peeled for pictures of her mother. But the photos	146–157
of so many teenagers distracted her. And to think that these	158–168
kids were now all adults!	169–173
Then Megan saw a picture of a student speaking at an	174–184
assembly. Though the hairstyle and clothing were unfamiliar to	185–193
Megan, it was clearly her mother.	194–199
"Dad, look!" Megan said.	200–203
Glancing over, her father asked, "You didn't know that your	204–213
mom was president of the student body?"	214–220

**EVALUATING CODES
FOR ORAL FLUENCY**

sky   (/) words read incorrectly

blue
^   sky   (^) inserted word
                       ( ]) after the last word

READING RATE AND ACCURACY

Total Words Read: _____

Number of Errors: _____

Number of Correct Words
Read Per Minute (WPM):   _____

Accuracy Rate: _____

(Number of Correct Words Read per
Minute ÷ Total Words Read)

READING FLUENCY

	Low	Average	High
Decoding ability	○	○	○
Pace	○	○	○
Syntax	○	○	○
Self-correction	○	○	○
Intonation	○	○	○

Record student rates on the Oral Fluency Scores pages.

Name _____ **Date** _____ **Score** _____

Narrative Writing

Writing Situation
A tradition in your family

Audience
Other students your age

Directions for Writing
Families have lots of traditions. Some of them have to do with special days, while others are about the family's past. Write a story about a tradition in your family. Try to write the story from the third-person point of view as if you were an outside observer.

Checklist
You will earn the best score if you
- think about the tradition and plan your writing before you begin.
- remember who will read your story.
- write in a way that is interesting to your readers.
- make sure your ideas flow in a way that makes sense.
- describe the tradition so the reader can understand it.
- use words that tell how you feel about the tradition.
- include enough details so the reader will understand the tradition.
- use correct capital letters, punctuation, and spelling.
- use subjects, verbs, and modifiers correctly.
- read your writing after you finish and check for mistakes.

Four Point Rubrics for Narrative Writing

Genre	1 Point	2 Points	3 Points	4 Points
Narrative	Narrative has missing details or elements. Logical order and narrative structure is unclear. Plot does not include a viable problem. Character development is not apparent. Setting does not include descriptions of where and when the narrative is set.	Narrative includes plot outline and some descriptive details and elements that add excitement or color, but narrative structure is not entirely clear. Character development is minimal. Setting includes minimal descriptions of where and when the narrative is set.	Narrative includes fairly well developed plot with descriptive details and other elements such as subplots that are integrated into the resolution. Narrative structure is clear. Characters are developed, though some characters may seem superficial. Setting includes descriptions of where and when the narrative is set.	Narrative includes more complicated plotlines with varied timelines, flashbacks, or dual story lines. Narrative structure is well defined. Characters well defined throughout, with unique qualities integral to the plot. Setting includes detailed descriptions of where and when the narrative is set.
Narrative: Theme	No theme is apparent.	Superficial theme is included but not integrated.	A theme is expressed but not well developed.	The narrative fully develops a theme that expresses an underlying message beyond the narrative plot.

Writing Traits

	1 Point	2 Points	3 Points	4 Points
Audience	Displays little or no sense of audience. Does not engage audience.	Displays some sense of audience.	Writes with audience in mind throughout.	Displays a strong sense of audience. Engages audience.
Voice	The writing provides little sense of involvement or commitment. There is no evidence that the writer has chosen a suitable voice.	The writer's commitment to the topic seems inconsistent. A sense of the writer may emerge at times; however, the voice is either inappropriately personal or impersonal.	A voice is present. The writer demonstrates commitment to the topic. In places, the writing is expressive, engaging, or sincere. Words and expressions are clear and precise.	The writer has chosen a voice appropriate for the topic, purpose, and audience. Unique style comes through. The writing is expressive, engaging, or sincere. Strong commitment to the topic.

Writing Conventions

	1 Point	2 Points	3 Points	4 Points
Conventions Overall	Numerous errors in usage, grammar, spelling, capitalization, and punctuation repeatedly distract the reader and make the text difficult to read. The reader finds it difficult to focus on the message.	The writing demonstrates limited control of standard writing conventions (punctuation, spelling, capitalization, grammar, and usage). Errors sometimes impede readability.	The writing demonstrates control of standard writing conventions (punctuation, spelling, capitalization, grammar, and usage). Minor errors, while perhaps noticeable, do not impede readability.	The writing demonstrates exceptionally strong control of standard writing conventions (punctuation, spelling, capitalization, grammar, and usage) and uses them effectively to enhance communication. Errors are so few and so minor that the reader can easily skim over them.

Name _____ Date _____ Score _____

The Sparks Fly

Vocabulary

Read each item. Fill in the bubble for the answer you think is correct.

1. What is the meaning of the prefix *in-?*

   Ⓐ half   Ⓒ before

   Ⓑ not   Ⓓ under

2. Another word for **dissolve** is

   Ⓐ pour.   Ⓒ spark.

   Ⓑ spread.   Ⓓ mix.

3. The scientist gave a **demonstration** on electricity. A **demonstration**

   Ⓐ discovers something new.

   Ⓑ fixes something that is broken.

   Ⓒ creates something as a team.

   Ⓓ shows how something works.

4. The Library Company received many strange objects from **donors. Donors** are people who

   Ⓐ ask important questions.

   Ⓑ give things away.

   Ⓒ want an education.

   Ⓓ are looking for work.

5. Heating systems in the 1700s were **inefficient.** If something is **inefficient,** it

   Ⓐ is unpopular.   Ⓒ works poorly.

   Ⓑ makes noise.   Ⓓ costs little.

The Sparks Fly (continued)

Comprehension

Read the following questions carefully. Then completely fill in the bubble of each correct answer. You may look back at the selection to find the answer to each of the questions.

1. In this selection, what seems to interest Franklin the most?

Ⓐ becoming a wealthy person

Ⓑ learning how things work

Ⓒ earning world-wide fame

Ⓓ helping those in need

2. The Library Company's first exhibition was

Ⓐ Thomas Penn's print of an orrery.

Ⓑ John Penn's air pump.

Ⓒ Franklin's cork spider.

Ⓓ a Leyden jar.

The Sparks Fly • **Lesson Assessment Book 1**

The Sparks Fly (continued)

3. What effect did Franklin's cork spider have on visitors?

   Ⓐ It gave them a mild electrical shock.

   Ⓑ It caused their hair to stand up.

   Ⓒ It sent a spark from their fingers.

   Ⓓ It made them jump in surprise.

4. Which of these helped Franklin discover that electricity was either *positive* or *negative*?

   Ⓐ People acted differently around demonstrations of electricity.

   Ⓑ Objects with an electric charge pushed away or attracted things.

   Ⓒ Sparks would fly out and make a hiss, crackle, and pop sound.

   Ⓓ Jars linked together with brass thread could cause electrical shock.

5. According to the selection, why did Franklin write *Experiments and Other Observations on Electricity Made at Philadelphia in America?*

   Ⓐ to share his discoveries with other scientists

   Ⓑ to claim that he had invented electricity

   Ⓒ to attract more people to his demonstrations

   Ⓓ to tell funny stories about his experiments

The Sparks Fly (continued)

Read the following questions carefully. Use complete sentences to answer the questions. Possible answers below

6. What details from the selection show that Franklin liked to have fun?

He made a cork spider jump for visitors. He electrified a painting.

7. What is the purpose of all the questions in the first paragraph?

To show the types of things that interested Franklin and types of questions he liked to ask.

8. Where did Franklin get information to satisfy his curiosity?

He read science books, and he wrote to and worked with other scientists.

9. What types of things did the Library Company have when it moved to the second floor of the new State House?

It had books, scientific tools, and objects such as fossils.

10. How did Franklin's interest in electricity compare with his interest in other subjects?

Although Franklin was interested in many things, he was most interested in electricity.

The Sparks Fly • **Lesson Assessment Book 1**

The Sparks Fly (continued)

Read the question below. Write complete sentences for your answer. Support your answer with information from the selection.

Linking to the Concepts How was Franklin's work with electricity important?

_____

_____

_____

_____

_____

Read the question below. Your answer should be based on your own experience. Write complete sentences for your answer.

Personal Response Which of the demonstrations described in the selection would you most liked to have attended? Explain your choice.

_____

_____

_____

_____

_____

_____

The Sparks Fly (continued)

Grammar, Usage, and Mechanics

Read each question. Fill in the bubble beside the answer in each group that is correct. If none of the answers is correct, choose the last answer, "none of the above."

1. Which sentence has correct punctuation?

    Ⓐ Five o'clock is when the city's only train arrives.

    Ⓑ Five o'clock is when the citys only train arrives.

    Ⓒ Five o'clock is when the citys' only train arrives.

    Ⓓ none of the above

2. Which sentence has correct punctuation?

    Ⓐ The lilies petals began to drop on the table.

    Ⓑ The lilie's petals began to drop on the table.

    Ⓒ The lilies's petals began to drop on the table.

    Ⓓ none of the above

3. In which sentence is a plural noun underlined?

    Ⓐ The <u>boss</u> answered the phone and yelled for Tom.

    Ⓑ In the <u>garden</u>, we grew tomatoes, onions, and peas.

    Ⓒ The brown <u>puppies</u> slept in a box by the fireplace.

    Ⓓ none of the above

4. Which sentence has correct plural forms?

    Ⓐ The friends all brought their lunchs to the park.

    Ⓑ Please pick up all the stickes and stones in the yard.

    Ⓒ Most small towns have at least two mailboxes.

    Ⓓ none of the above

5. Which is an example of an action verb?

    Ⓐ am   Ⓒ will

    Ⓑ throw   Ⓓ none of the above

The Sparks Fly (continued)

Analyzing the Selection

Read the questions below. Write complete sentences for your answer. Support your answer with information from the selection.

What do you think people thought of Franklin during his life? Why do you think they thought this way?

_____

_____

_____

_____

_____

_____

_____

_____

_____

_____

_____

_____

_____

_____

_____

_____

_____

The Sparks Fly (continued)

Oral Fluency Assessment

Emerson's Adventure

Emerson rode with her mother and little sister in the family	1–11
station wagon. Her father and brother were behind them in	12–21
the truck with the big, black tubes piled in the back. With each	22–34
passing mile, Emerson smiled more and more. She imagined	35–43
the fun and excitement they would have. They would float	44–53
down the river splashing each other and looking at the nature	54–64
around them. They finally reached Tom's Fork and parked the	65–74
car. Emerson jumped out quickly. She could not wait for the	75–85
adventure to start.	86–88
"Not so fast, Emerson," said her mother. "Remember, we're	89–97
just here to leave the car. We still have to drive up the river.	98–111
After we float back here, we'll be able to drive the car upstream	112–124
to the truck."	125–127
"Oh, yeah, false alarm," Emerson said. She had forgotten the	128–137
family's plan to leave one car at each end of the float.	138–149
Once the whole family was in the truck, they set out for	150–161
Jenkins Bar, a sandy beach on a wide part of the river. It did not	162–176
take very long to get there on the road. But because the river has	177–190
many winding turns and the current is kind of slow, it was going	191–203
to take them about three hours to float back to Tom's Fork.	204–215
"That's three wonderful hours of tubing," thought Emerson.	216–223

EVALUATING CODES FOR ORAL FLUENCY

sky   (/) words read incorrectly

blue
^ sky   (^) inserted word
     ( ]) after the last word

READING RATE AND ACCURACY

Total Words Read: _____

Number of Errors: _____

Number of Correct Words
Read Per Minute (WPM): _____

Accuracy Rate: _____

(Number of Correct Words Read per Minute ÷ Total Words Read)

READING FLUENCY

	Low	Average	High
Decoding ability	O	O	O
Pace	O	O	O
Syntax	O	O	O
Self-correction	O	O	O
Intonation	O	O	O

Record student rates on the Oral Fluency Scores pages.

Name _____ Date _____ Score _____

Tailing Tornadoes

Vocabulary

Read each item. Fill in the bubble for the answer you think is correct.

1. Another word for **severe** is
   Ⓐ dangerous. Ⓒ quiet.
   Ⓑ quick. Ⓓ smooth.

2. Which word contains the Latin root meaning "to see"?
   Ⓐ credible Ⓒ television
   Ⓑ sense Ⓓ science

3. Tornadoes are **raging** columns of wind. What does **raging** mean in this sentence?
   Ⓐ curved and rounded
   Ⓑ long and narrow
   Ⓒ amazing and thrilling
   Ⓓ active and powerful

4. Greg took a **survey** of the morning sky. In this sentence, a **survey** is
   Ⓐ a travel map. Ⓒ a quick drawing.
   Ⓑ a careful look. Ⓓ a scientific question.

5. As a meteorologist, Greg thinks tornadoes are an **inspiration.** An **inspiration** is
   Ⓐ a stirring of the mind.
   Ⓑ a dangerous experiment.
   Ⓒ a problem with nature.
   Ⓓ a strange hobby.

Tailing Tornadoes (continued)

Comprehension

Read the following questions carefully. Then completely fill in the bubble of each correct answer. You may look back at the selection to find the answer to each of the questions.

1. The main reason Greg chases tornadoes is

   Ⓐ because experiencing tornadoes is exciting.

   Ⓑ so people can know more about tornadoes.

   Ⓒ so tornadoes can someday be prevented.

   Ⓓ because tornadoes are his hobby.

2. Which two things help to form cumulonimbus clouds or thunderheads?

   Ⓐ tornadoes and twisters

   Ⓑ warm air and cool air

   Ⓒ spirals and stovepipes

   Ⓓ storms and storm chasers

Tailing Tornadoes (continued)

3. Why does Greg pick up Bill on his way to the target area?

Ⓐ He knows that it is safer to chase in pairs.

Ⓑ He wants to show Bill an example of chasing.

Ⓒ He needs someone to photograph the chase.

Ⓓ He thinks Bill knows his way around Texas.

4. What is the first clue that Greg and Bill are getting close to the tornado?

Ⓐ They see a wall cloud start to swirl.

Ⓑ They notice anvil clouds forming.

Ⓒ They see some cumulonimbus clouds.

Ⓓ They watch a funnel cloud start to form.

5. The author most likely wrote this selection to

Ⓐ compare a tornado with a twister.

Ⓑ share a tornado tale from long ago.

Ⓒ explain how to survive a tornado.

Ⓓ inform readers about tornadoes and their study.

Tailing Tornadoes (continued)

Read the following questions carefully. Use complete sentences to answer the questions. Possible answers below

6. What helps to make a vortex visible?

   If a vortex contains cloud droplets or debris, it can be seen.

7. What is the ham radio used for during a chase?

   It is used to stay in touch with the National Weather Service and storm spotters.

8. Why do some tornadoes make noise and others do not?

   A tornado's sound depends on what it hits and what the air passes through.

9. Why does the author write that the tornado starts to "rope out" before disappearing?

   He writes this because it becomes long and skinny like a rope.

10. On the lines below, write one fact about tornadoes from the selection.

   Tornado Alley is a region in central North America.

Tailing Tornadoes (continued)

Read the question below. Write complete sentences for your answer. Support your answer with information from the selection.

Linking to the Concepts If being hit by a tornado is not the main threat to storm chasers, what *is* the main threat?

_____

_____

_____

_____

_____

Read the questions below. Your answer should be based on your own experience. Write complete sentences for your answer.

Personal Response Would you like to be a storm chaser? Why?

_____

_____

_____

_____

_____

Tailing Tornadoes (continued)

Grammar, Usage, and Mechanics

Read each question. Fill in the bubble beside the answer in each group that is correct. If none of the answers is correct, choose the last answer, "none of the above."

1. When you search for information with a computer, which of these is most helpful?

   Ⓐ a comma   Ⓒ **a keyword**

   Ⓑ a rhyme   Ⓓ none of the above

2. Which Internet site would probably give you the best information about Yellowstone National Park?

   Ⓐ the National Center on Education

   Ⓑ the National High School Athletic Association

   Ⓒ the National Park Service

   Ⓓ none of the above

3. If you searched for "pet fish," which of these would you probably find?

   Ⓐ **goldfish**   Ⓒ dolphins

   Ⓑ whales   Ⓓ none of the above

4. Which search words would help you find news in other countries?

   Ⓐ school news   Ⓒ local news

   Ⓑ **world news**   Ⓓ none of the above

5. Which sentence contains a coordinating conjunction?

   Ⓐ Before you go, leave me the book.

   Ⓑ I did the laundry, and Jack folded clothes.

   Ⓒ We went into the library.

   Ⓓ none of the above

Tailing Tornadoes (continued)

Analyzing the Selection

Read the question below. Write complete sentences for your answer. Support your answer with information from the selection.

Do you think storm chasers are real scientists whose work helps people? Explain your opinion thoroughly.

_____

_____

_____

_____

_____

_____

_____

_____

_____

_____

_____

_____

_____

_____

Tailing Tornadoes (continued)

Oral Fluency Assessment

The Cell Phone

As they walked to the movie theater, Russell and Patricia	1–10
talked about film. Russell wanted to see a mystery, but Patricia	11–21
was voting for science fiction.	22–26
"Listen to that," said Russell, looking around. A small voice	27–36
was coming from under the nearby hedges.	37–43
Bending down, Patricia and Russell heard the voice say, "To	44–53
listen to your messages, press the star button." The voice was	54–64
from a cell phone!	65–68
Patricia found the phone and said, "Someone must have lost	69–78
this. How do we figure out who the owner is?"	79–88
The two were stumped, and then Patricia suggested,	89–96
"Russell, find the list of numbers in the cell phone."	97–106
"Okay," said Russell, "but I doubt the owner is listed there."	107–117
"Now look for a listing for 'ICE' and call that number,"	118–128
Patricia said.	129–130
Scrolling through the menu, Russell exclaimed, "Hey! How	131–138
did you know ICE would be listed here?"	139–146
Patricia explained that ICE stood for *In Case of Emergency*.	147–156
Nodding, Russell called ICE, and a man answered. Russell	157–165
explained that he had found the phone and asked the man if he	166–178
knew whose phone it was.	179–183
The man said, "Thank you, so much! My daughter has been	184–194
looking everywhere for it." He then told Russell that he would	195–205
meet him at the movie theater shortly.	206–212

EVALUATING CODES FOR ORAL FLUENCY

sky   (/) words read incorrectly

blue
   ^   sky   (^) inserted word
                ( ]) after the last word

READING RATE AND ACCURACY

Total Words Read: _____

Number of Errors: _____

Number of Correct Words Read Per Minute (WPM): _____

Accuracy Rate: _____

(Number of Correct Words Read per Minute ÷ Total Words Read)

READING FLUENCY

	Low	Average	High
Decoding ability	O	O	O
Pace	O	O	O
Syntax	O	O	O
Self-correction	O	O	O
Intonation	O	O	O

Record student rates on the Oral Fluency Scores pages.

Name _____ Date _____ Score _____

Jake Drake Know-It-All

Vocabulary

Read each item. Fill in the bubble for the answer you think is correct.

1. What word best completes the following word relationship?

_____, **theory, scientific method**

    (A) newspaper   (C) light

    (B) animals   (D) hypothesis

2. Another word for **practically** is

    (A) really.   (C) carefully.

    (B) nearly.   (D) neatly.

3. To finish their science project, the boys must write their **conclusions.** In this sentence, **conclusions** are

    (A) why an experiment was needed.

    (B) how an experiment was done.

    (C) what is learned from an experiment.

    (D) who is in charge of an experiment.

4. Willie **squinted** when Jake said something puzzling. **Squinted** means that he

    (A) made a strange sound.

    (B) closed his eyes partway.

    (C) waved his arms.

    (D) sat down and thought.

5. Willie wanted to **observe** how different balls bounced. In this sentence, **observe** means

    (A) to practice a new skill.   (C) to change something.

    (B) to teach others.   (D) to make a careful study.

Jake Drake Know-It-All (continued)

Comprehension

Read the following questions carefully. Then completely fill in the bubble of each correct answer. You may look back at the selection to find the answer to each of the questions.

1. Which statement is true about Jake's dad?

   Ⓐ He works at the school.

   Ⓑ He wants to be helpful.

   Ⓒ He knows all about electromagnets.

   Ⓓ He thinks his own ideas are best.

2. Jake persuades Mrs. Snavin to let Willie be his partner by

   Ⓐ pointing out the rules in the science fair booklet.

   Ⓑ promising to do an excellent science fair project.

   Ⓒ telling her that his current partner is sick.

   Ⓓ saying that they had already been working together.

Jake Drake Know-It-All (continued)

3. Willie is surprised when Jake tells him they are partners because Willie thought Jake had

    Ⓐ started with another partner.

    Ⓑ thought the ball idea was silly.

    Ⓒ wanted to work by himself.

    Ⓓ waited until the last week.

4. Why does Jake think he and Willie are like magnets?

    Ⓐ They stick together.

    Ⓑ They like junkyards.

    Ⓒ They are drawn to sports.

    Ⓓ They laugh at the same stuff.

5. The cans were useful in the boys' project for all of these reasons EXCEPT

    Ⓐ they had weights on them.

    Ⓑ they were made of steel.

    Ⓒ they could be stacked together.

    Ⓓ they contained food.

Jake Drake Know-It-All (continued)

Read the following questions carefully. Use complete sentences to answer the questions. Possible answers below

6. What was the first step in Jake and Willie's science fair project?

They had to come up with a hypothesis.

7. How does Jake finally make his father feel included?

He invites his dad to look at the nails once they are wound with wire.

8. What does Jake think of his friend Willie?

He thinks Willie has good ideas and is fun to work with.

9. What is a fact about Mrs. Karp? What is an opinion about Mrs. Drinkwater?

Karp is the principal. Drinkwater runs the school most of the time.

10. Why do you think the author ends the selection the way that he does?

He wants the reader to know that science can be hard work, but it is also fun.

Jake Drake Know-It-All (continued)

Read the question below. Write complete sentences for your answer. Support your answer with information from the selection.

Linking to the Concepts In what ways is Jake a good leader?

_____

_____

_____

_____

_____

_____

Read the question below. Your answer should be based on your own experience. Write complete sentences for your answer.

Personal Response Would you like to be Jake's partner? Explain your answer using details from the selection.

_____

_____

_____

_____

_____

_____

Jake Drake Know-It-All (continued)

Grammar, Usage, and Mechanics

Read each question. Fill in the bubble beside the answer in each group that is correct. If none of the answers is correct, choose the last answer, "none of the above."

1. Which sentence contains a pronoun?

   Ⓐ Wanda and I are planning to go along too.

   Ⓑ How many people is Jacob going to take?

   Ⓒ Three more people can ride in the van.

   Ⓓ none of the above

2. Which sentence contains a possessive pronoun?

   Ⓐ The suitcases should fit.

   Ⓑ That suitcase is mine.

   Ⓒ Can you get the car packed?

   Ⓓ none of the above

3. Which sentence contains a subject pronoun?

   Ⓐ We are not ready to leave yet.

   Ⓑ Give Jacob his suitcase to carry.

   Ⓒ Her suitcases are over there.

   Ⓓ none of the above

4. Which sentence contains an object pronoun?

   Ⓐ Mia and her sister went with Tina.

   Ⓑ Mia's sister forgot her dress shoes.

   Ⓒ Tina lent her a pair of shoes.

   Ⓓ none of the above

5. Which pronoun can take the place of the underlined part in this sentence?
   Tristan and I were upset because we could not go.

   Ⓐ We

   Ⓑ He

   Ⓒ Us

   Ⓓ none of the above

Jake Drake Know-It-All (continued)

Analyzing the Selection

Read the questions below. Write complete sentences for your answer. Support your answer with information from the selections.

What types of traits do you need to be a scientist? Why? Support your answer with information from the selections you have read in this unit.

_____

_____

_____

_____

_____

_____

_____

_____

_____

_____

_____

_____

_____

_____

Jake Drake Know-It-All (continued)

Oral Fluency Assessment

Meeting a New Friend

"May I sit here?" asked Roger in an unusual voice. He signed while he talked. It was a little difficult to understand him. — 1–12 / 13–23

"Sure," answered Patsy. She was very nervous. Her words barely came out. "What am I supposed to do?" she asked herself. "I've never met a hearing-impaired person before." — 24–32 / 33–43 / 44–52

All that morning, Patsy had a hard time paying attention. She kept looking over at Roger. He seemed to be able to understand what was going on in class. "How does he do that?" she wondered to herself. — 53–62 / 63–74 / 75–86 / 87–90

At lunch, Roger sat beside Patsy. Her two friends, Amos and Tara, were there also. Roger smiled and started talking. It was difficult for them at first. But by the end of lunch, they knew a little bit more about each other. — 91–101 / 102–112 / 113–126 / 127–132

That afternoon, Mrs. Martin took some time to let Roger and the other students get to know each other better. Patsy was surprised to find that one of her other friends, Kyle, actually knew sign language. Patsy also found herself trying to explain what Roger was saying when the others couldn't understand. — 133–143 / 144–154 / 155–165 / 166–175 / 176–184

That afternoon, Roger and Patsy walked home together for a few blocks. Patsy learned some signs. She told Roger about her family. By the time she reached the corner of her street, she was able to sign "good-bye." — 185–194 / 195–205 / 206–217 / 218–223

EVALUATING CODES FOR ORAL FLUENCY

sky — (/) words read incorrectly

blue
^ sky — (^) inserted word
( ]) after the last word

READING RATE AND ACCURACY

Total Words Read: _____

Number of Errors: _____

Number of Correct Words Read Per Minute (WPM): _____

Accuracy Rate: _____

(Number of Correct Words Read per Minute ÷ Total Words Read)

READING FLUENCY

	Low	Average	High
Decoding ability	O	O	O
Pace	O	O	O
Syntax	O	O	O
Self-correction	O	O	O
Intonation	O	O	O

Record student rates on the Oral Fluency Scores pages.

Name _____ **Date** _____ **Score** _____

The Wind at Work

Vocabulary

Read each item. Fill in the bubble for the answer you think is correct.

1. If something **expands,** it becomes

Ⓐ larger.   Ⓒ louder.

Ⓑ softer.   Ⓓ faster.

2. What does the prefix **re-** mean?

Ⓐ into   Ⓒ again

Ⓑ not   Ⓓ down from

3. The **flickering** lanterns could be seen during the storm. **Flickering** means

Ⓐ shining extra brightly.

Ⓑ going on and off quickly.

Ⓒ banging against each other.

Ⓓ bouncing up and down.

4. The wind helps to **propel** sailboats on the water. To **propel** something means to

Ⓐ protect it.   Ⓒ move it forward.

Ⓑ anchor it.   Ⓓ keep it balanced.

5. A set of turbines **converts** wind energy into electricity. In this sentence, **converts** means

Ⓐ stores something for future use.

Ⓑ makes something out of nothing.

Ⓒ traps something and gets rid of it safely.

Ⓓ changes something into something else.

The Wind at Work (continued)

Comprehension

Read the following questions carefully. Then completely fill in the bubble of each correct answer. You may look back at the selection to find the answer to each of the questions.

1. The Dutch most likely called the sea the Waterwolf because

Ⓐ the sea was shaped like a wolf.

🅑 the sea was threatening like a wolf.

Ⓑ the sea sounded like a wolf.

Ⓓ the sea moved like a wolf.

2. Which of these devices was the first to harness the power of the wind?

Ⓐ kites

Ⓑ turbines

🅒 sailboats

Ⓓ windmills

The Wind at Work (continued)

3. Wind is caused by

Ⓐ the sun warming Earth unevenly.

Ⓑ the turning of windmill sails.

Ⓒ the rotation of Earth.

Ⓓ the great distance between the equator and the poles.

4. The selection suggests that wind is not a perfect source of energy because

Ⓐ it is costly to harness.

Ⓑ it is not as abundant as coal.

Ⓒ it causes damage.

Ⓓ it is difficult to predict the amount of wind.

5. According to the selection, why were windmills so popular?

Ⓐ They were a sign of wealth.

Ⓑ They made heavy jobs easier.

Ⓒ They were easy to transport.

Ⓓ They helped predict weather.

The Wind at Work (continued)

Read the following questions carefully. Use complete sentences to answer the questions. Possible answers below

6. What would be the effect of having wind turbines produce ten percent of America's electrical power?

It would stop pollution made by nine hundred thousand tons of fossil fuel.

7. What does it mean when the author writes that wind is a "renewable energy"?

It means that wind power is an energy source we cannot use up.

8. According to the author, what do today's wind turbines look like?

They look like giant airplane propellers or like toy pinwheels.

9. What are two reasons the wind is a good source of energy?

It is renewable; it does not cause pollution; it is safe; it is free.

10. What replaced the windmill in Europe in the 1800s?

The steam engine replaced the windmill.

The Wind at Work (continued)

Read the question below. Write complete sentences for your answer. Support your answer with information from the selection.

Linking to the Concepts How has wind been valuable to people throughout history?

_____

_____

_____

_____

_____

_____

Read the questions below. Your answer should be based on your own experience. Write complete sentences for your answer.

Personal Response Do you like being outside when it is windy? Why or why not?

_____

_____

_____

_____

_____

_____

The Wind at Work (continued)

Grammar, Usage, and Mechanics

Read each question. Fill in the bubble beside the answer in each group that is correct. If none of the answers is correct, choose the last answer, "none of the above."

1. Which of these is a compound sentence?
   - Ⓐ The carnival is held on the town playground every year.
   - Ⓑ Many groups and individuals set up stands there.
   - Ⓒ The children enjoy the rides, and the adults buy crafts.
   - Ⓓ none of the above

2. Which of these is a compound sentence?
   - Ⓐ Everyone loves the many choices food stands offer.
   - Ⓑ After dark, the lights on the Ferris wheel come on.
   - Ⓒ Even small children are allowed to stay up late.
   - Ⓓ none of the above

3. Which sentence has correct punctuation?
   - Ⓐ Tonya has a beautiful voice; she will sing the solo.
   - Ⓑ Tonya has a beautiful voice she will sing the solo.
   - Ⓒ Tonya has a beautiful voice she will sing; the solo.
   - Ⓓ none of the above

4. What is the best way to combine these two sentences?
   The storm is almost over. It is still raining lightly.
   - Ⓐ The storm is almost, over but it is still raining lightly.
   - Ⓑ The storm is almost over, but it is still raining lightly.
   - Ⓒ The storm is almost over but, it is still raining lightly.
   - Ⓓ none of the above

5. Which is an example of an irregular plural?
   - Ⓐ beds
   - Ⓒ dishes
   - Ⓑ geese
   - Ⓓ taxes

The Wind at Work (continued)

Analyzing the Selection

Read the questions below. Write complete sentences for your answer. Support your answer with information from the selection.

What do you think the future of wind power is? Will people accept wind generators near their homes?

_____

_____

_____

_____

_____

_____

_____

_____

_____

_____

_____

_____

_____

_____

The Wind at Work (continued)

Oral Fluency Assessment

Out of Shape

As Ollie pedaled his bike, he noticed something unusual.	1–9
He was climbing the short hill to his house, just as he had done	10–23
a hundred times before. However, for some reason, it was	24–33
taking a tremendous effort to make the bike's pedals go around.	34–44
Ollie wondered, "How did I get so out of shape?"	45–54
In the driveway, he got off and pushed the bike into the	55–66
garage. Ollie went into the house and got a glass of fruit juice.	67–79
He called out, "Mom, I'm going to try out for the school's track	80–92
team after all!"	93–95
Ollie's mother came into the kitchen and patted his	96–104
shoulder. "That's wonderful, but why did you change your	105–113
mind?" she inquired.	114–116
His mother listened as Ollie explained the difficulty biking	117–125
home. Then she left the kitchen and disappeared for a couple of	126–137
minutes. When she returned, she had a knowing smile.	138–146
"Ollie, I would love to see you go out for track, but just so	147–160
you know, you're not as out of shape as you think," she said.	161–173
Puzzled, Ollie asked, "How do you know that?"	174–181
"I went out to the garage to check your bike," she answered	182–193
with a chuckle. "Your tires were very low on air, so I pumped	194–206
them up again. I think that the next time you pedal home, you'll	207–219
feel more fit!"	220–222

EVALUATING CODES FOR ORAL FLUENCY

sky   (/) words read incorrectly

blue
 ^   sky   (^) inserted word
          ( ]) after the last word

READING RATE AND ACCURACY

Total Words Read: _____

Number of Errors: _____

Number of Correct Words
Read Per Minute (WPM):   _____

Accuracy Rate: _____

(Number of Correct Words Read per Minute ÷ Total Words Read)

READING FLUENCY

	Low	Average	High
Decoding ability	O	O	O
Pace	O	O	O
Syntax	O	O	O
Self-correction	O	O	O
Intonation	O	O	O

Record student rates on the Oral Fluency Scores pages.

Name _____ Date _____ Score _____

What Are Food Chains and Webs?

Vocabulary

Read each item. Fill in the bubble for the answer you think is correct.

1. What does the Latin root **vor** mean?

Ⓐ to eat   Ⓒ to see

Ⓑ to breathe   Ⓓ to travel

2. The word **absorbs** means

Ⓐ stays away.   Ⓒ lifts up.

Ⓑ takes in.   Ⓓ turns over.

3. A vulture is a **scavenger.** A **scavenger** is an animal that

Ⓐ eats according to the changing seasons.

Ⓑ feeds on plants only.

Ⓒ eats both plants and animals.

Ⓓ feeds on animals that are no longer alive.

4. Some grass-eating animals have **ridges** on their teeth for grinding food. **Ridges** are

Ⓐ smooth places.   Ⓒ raised edges.

Ⓑ colored spots.   Ⓓ small cracks.

5. Most meat-eating animals are **predators. Predators** are animals that

Ⓐ feed only at night.

Ⓑ hunt other animals for food.

Ⓒ eat meat only during the summer.

Ⓓ care for and feed their young.

What Are Food Chains and Webs? (continued)

Comprehension

Read the following questions carefully. Then completely fill in the bubble of each correct answer. You may look back at the selection to find the answer to each of the questions.

1. Which of these is an example of an ecosystem?

Ⓐ a berry

Ⓑ a chipmunk

Ⓒ an owl

Ⓓ a woodland

2. All of the following can be placed in the "Carnivore" category EXCEPT

Ⓐ rabbits.

Ⓑ tigers.

Ⓒ lynx.

Ⓓ weasels.

What Are Food Chains and Webs? (continued)

3. What do herbivores have in common?

    Ⓐ They are eaten by nothing else in the food web.

    Ⓑ They are the largest animals in the food chain.

    Ⓒ They are the primary consumers in the food chain.

    Ⓓ They are consumers that eat both plants and animals.

4. Why are decomposers called "nature's clean-up crew"?

    Ⓐ They are found in the water.

    Ⓑ They get rid of dead material.

    Ⓒ They prevent slime mold.

    Ⓓ They have a nice smell.

5. The selection lists sheep, cows, and deer as examples of animals that

    Ⓐ eat primarily animals.

    Ⓑ must chew their food twice.

    Ⓒ get their nutrients from the soil.

    Ⓓ use photosynthesis to feed themselves.

What Are Food Chains and Webs? (continued)

Read the following questions carefully. Use complete sentences to answer the questions. Possible answers below

6. What are two important things that plants provide animals and people?

They provide food/energy; they provide oxygen; they provide water.

7. How do meat-eating plants differ from most other plants?

They do not get all of the nutrients they need from the soil, so they eat insects.

8. Why is food so important to living things?

Food provides nutrients for the body, and it provides energy to do things.

9. How is the energy from the sun passed along the food chain?

Plants trap the energy, animals eat the plants, and other animals eat them.

10. Why are there fewer living things on the last level of a food web or energy pyramid?

There is only enough energy to keep a few carnivores alive.

What Are Food Chains and Webs? (continued)

Read the question below. Write complete sentences for your answer. Support your answer with information from the selection.

Linking to the Concepts Why are the terms "chain" and "web" useful in describing the way food moves in and out of ecosystems?

_____

_____

_____

_____

Read the question below. Your answer should be based on your own experience. Write complete sentences for your answer.

Personal Response What evidence is there of food chains and food webs in your immediate neighborhood?

_____

_____

_____

_____

UNIT 2 Lesson 5

What Are Food Chains and Webs? (continued)

Grammar, Usage, and Mechanics

Read each question. Fill in the bubble beside the answer in each group that is correct. If none of the answers is correct, choose the last answer, "none of the above."

1. In which item is a possessive noun underlined?

Ⓐ the puppy's basket Ⓒ the China patterns

Ⓑ the flowers on the table Ⓓ none of the above

2. In which sentence is a possessive plural noun underlined?

Ⓐ Dozens of tadpoles swam in the pond.

Ⓑ The tadpoles' legs are starting to grow.

Ⓒ One tadpole's tail is almost gone.

Ⓓ none of the above

3. Which sentence contains a subject pronoun?

Ⓐ Brian wanted everyone to come to the game with him.

Ⓑ His brother, Jack, plays on the school football team.

Ⓒ They made plans to watch Jack play this Friday.

Ⓓ none of the above

4. Which sentence contains an object pronoun?

Ⓐ The quarterback threw him a long pass.

Ⓑ He caught the ball and ran for a touchdown.

Ⓒ We all cheered loudly when we won the game.

Ⓓ none of the above

5. Which of these is a compound sentence?

Ⓐ The woods were filled with fallen trees after the storm.

Ⓑ Although we were stuck, the animals leaped over the trees.

Ⓒ Workers with trucks and men with axes came to help.

Ⓓ none of the above

What Are Food Chains and Webs? (continued)

Analyzing the Selection

Read the prompt below. Write complete sentences for your response. Support your response with information from the selections.

Even though "What Are Food Chains and Webs?" is about energy, it is very different from the other selections in this unit. Explain some ways this selection is different from the others. Point out any ways you think this selection is similar to the others.

_____

_____

_____

_____

_____

_____

_____

_____

_____

_____

_____

_____

_____

_____

What Are Food Chains and Webs? (continued)

Oral Fluency Assessment

Jacob Miller's Children

Jacob Miller looked at his children playing outside their	1–9
home. He was worried about their future, but knew there was	10–20
almost nothing he could do about it. As a poor English farmer in	21–33
the year 1564, his greatest worry was putting food on the table.	34–45
"Daydreaming again, Jacob?" Abigail Miller smiled at her	46–53
husband as she kneaded the bread she would bake in the large	54–65
fireplace that filled almost an entire wall. She knew that her	66–76
husband was a thinker and a daydreamer. She knew that his	77–87
mind often wandered.	88–90
"It saddens me to think about our children. There's not much	91–101
of a life waiting for them. The boys will barely make a living	102–114
farming someone else's land. The girls will marry equally poor	115–124
husbands. It's a terrible shame. They are such bright children.	125–134
They deserve better."	135–137
Jacob looked at his wife and smiled. She was a wonderful	138–148
woman. He loved her dearly. She was the best thing that had	149–160
ever happened to him. He wished he could do more for her.	161–172
"I know it sounds foolish, Abigail, but I would like the	173–183
children to learn to read and write. We can't afford to send them	184–196
to school, but isn't there some way they can learn their letters	197–208
and numbers? It's a fine ability to have."	209–216

**EVALUATING CODES
FOR ORAL FLUENCY**

sky (/) words read incorrectly

blue
 ^   sky   (^) inserted word
        ( ]) after the last word

READING RATE AND ACCURACY

Total Words Read: _____

Number of Errors: _____

Number of Correct Words
Read Per Minute (WPM): _____

Accuracy Rate: _____

(Number of Correct Words Read per
Minute ÷ Total Words Read)

READING FLUENCY

	Low	Average	High
Decoding ability	○	○	○
Pace	○	○	○
Syntax	○	○	○
Self-correction	○	○	○
Intonation	○	○	○

Record student rates on the Oral Fluency Scores pages.

Name _____ **Date** _____ **Score** _____

Expository Writing

Writing Situation
A weather event you remember

Audience
Your classmates

Directions for Writing
All of us remember an interesting weather event. It might be a storm, a really cold day, or a very beautiful day. Think about an interesting weather day. Write a description of the day. Explain the type of weather and why you think it is interesting. Include details so the reader will have a good picture of the weather you are describing.

Checklist
You will earn the best score if you
- choose an interesting weather event.
- describe the event in the first paragraph.
- make sure your ideas flow in a way that makes sense.
- use sensory words and figurative language so the reader can experience the event.
- write more sentences and longer sentences when you revise.
- avoid words and phrases that are often overused.
- use correct capital letters, punctuation, and spelling.
- use subjects, verbs, and modifiers correctly.
- write complete sentences and avoid fragments or run-ons.
- read your writing after you finish and check for mistakes.

Four Point Rubrics for Expository Writing

Genre	1 Point	2 Points	3 Points	4 Points
Expository	Composition has no introduction or clear topic. It offers a group of loosely related facts or a series of poorly written steps. No conclusion is included.	Composition is clearly organized around main points with supportive facts or assertions. Composition has no clear introduction, but its topic is identifiable. However, it includes many facts unrelated to the topic, or it describes things in a disorganized way. No conclusion is included.	Main points and supportive details can be identified, but they are not clearly marked. Composition has an introduction and offers facts about the topic. Some facts may be irrelevant, or some ideas may be vague or out of order. The report is fairly well organized but doesn't have a strong conclusion.	Traces and constructs a line of argument, identifying part-to-whole relations. Main points are supported with logical and appropriate evidence. Composition begins with an introduction and offers relevant facts about the topic or describes the topic appropriately. The report is organized using cause/effect, comparison/ contrast, or another pattern. It ends with a strong conclusion.
Writing Traits				
Focus	Topic is unclear or wanders and must be inferred. Extraneous material may be present.	Topic/position/direction is unclear and must be inferred.	Topic/position is stated and direction/ purpose is previewed and maintained. Mainly stays on topic.	Topic/position is clearly stated, previewed, and maintained throughout the paper. Topics and details are tied together with a central theme or purpose that is maintained /threaded throughout the paper.
Ideas/Content	Superficial and/or minimal content is included.	Main ideas are understandable, although they may be overly broad or simplistic, and the results may not be effective. Supporting detail is limited, insubstantial, overly general or off topic.	The writing is clear and focused. The reader can easily understand the main ideas. Support is present, although it may be limited or rather general.	Writing is exceptionally clear, focused, and interesting. Main ideas stand out and are developed by strong support and rich details.
Elaboration (supporting details and examples that develop the main idea)	States ideas or points with minimal detail to support them.	Includes sketchy, redundant, or general details; some may be irrelevant. Support for key ideas is very uneven.	Includes mix of general statements and specific details/examples. Support is mostly relevant but may be uneven and lack depth in places.	Includes specific details and supporting examples for each key point/idea. May use compare/contrast to support.
Writing Conventions				
Conventions Overall	Numerous errors in usage, grammar, spelling, capitalization, and punctuation repeatedly distract the reader and make the text difficult to read. The reader finds it difficult to focus on the message.	The writing demonstrates limited control of standard writing conventions (punctuation, spelling, capitalization, grammar, and usage). Errors sometimes impede readability.	The writing demonstrates control of standard writing conventions (punctuation, spelling, capitalization, grammar, and usage). Minor errors, while perhaps noticeable, do not impede readability.	The writing demonstrates exceptionally strong control of standard writing conventions (punctuation, spelling, capitalization, grammar, and usage) and uses them effectively to enhance communication. Errors are so few and so minor that the reader can easily skim over them.

Name _____ Date _____ Score _____

. . . If You Lived at the Time of the American Revolution

Vocabulary

Read each item. Fill in the bubble for the answer you think is correct.

1. The inflectional ending **-ed** in *cooked* tells you that the action

   Ⓐ will happen soon.   Ⓒ is happening right now.

   Ⓑ happened in the past.   Ⓓ cannot happen.

2. **Pamphlets** are a type of

   Ⓐ organization.   Ⓒ speech.

   Ⓑ lesson.   Ⓓ book.

3. About one-third of the people living in the colonies remained **loyal** to England. **Loyal** means that the people

   Ⓐ supported England.

   Ⓑ went to England frequently.

   Ⓒ had to pay taxes to England.

   Ⓓ wrote stories about England.

4. Some men fought with the **militia. A militia** is a

   Ⓐ large type of gun.

   Ⓑ group of citizens trained to fight.

   Ⓒ group of foreign soldiers.

   Ⓓ boat that takes soldiers to battle.

5. Deborah Sampson got a **discharge** from the army for her work as a soldier. This means that she got a(n)

   Ⓐ order to serve as a nurse instead.   Ⓒ dismissal from service.

   Ⓑ large amount of money.   Ⓓ uniform.

. . . If You Lived at the Time of the American Revolution (continued)

Comprehension

Read the following questions carefully. Then completely fill in the bubble of each correct answer. You may look back at the selection to find the answer to each of the questions.

1. Which of these is not a name for the war which freed the colonies?

   (A) the American Revolution

   (B) the War of Independence

   (C) the War of the States

   (D) the Revolutionary War

2. Who were the "Lobsterbacks"?

   (A) the British soldiers

   (B) the Patriot militia

   (C) the men behind the Boston Tea Party

   (D) the Boston Massacre victims

. . . If You Lived at the Time of the American Revolution (continued)

3. Which of these was a type of business common in the Middle Colonies?

  Ⓐ shipbuilding

  Ⓑ farming

  Ⓒ fishing

  Ⓓ whale hunting

4. What caused the Boston Tea Party?

  Ⓐ There was too much tea in the Colonies.

  Ⓑ It was a celebration after the states declared their freedom.

  Ⓒ The Loyalists were celebrating a popular British holiday.

  Ⓓ There was a tax on tea paid to the British.

5. What happened right after the Boston Massacre?

  Ⓐ The Stamp Act was repealed.

  Ⓑ The Declaration of Independence was signed.

  Ⓒ New York City became known as the Tory capital of America.

  Ⓓ Many people joined the Patriots.

. . . If You Lived at the Time of the American Revolution (continued)

Read the following questions carefully. Use complete sentences to answer the questions. Possible answers below

6. Why is the Fourth of July a holiday?

It was the day that the Declaration of Independence was signed in 1776.

7. What is the difference between a Loyalist and a Patriot?

Loyalists remained loyal to England; Patriots wanted a new nation.

8. Name two reasons the author gives as to why people stayed loyal to England.

They believed the king had the right to rule; they feared British soldiers.

9. How was Benjamin Franklin different from his son, William?

Benjamin Franklin was a well-known Patriot. His son was a Loyalist.

10. Why did Deborah Sampson dress in men's clothes and change her name to Robert Shurtleff?

Deborah Sampson wanted to serve in the fight for independence.

. . . If You Lived at the Time of the American Revolution (continued)

Read the question below. Write complete sentences for your answer. Support your answer with information from the selection.

Linking to the Concepts How did the Declaration of Independence change the lives of the colonists?

_____

_____

_____

_____

Read the question below. Your answer should be based on your own experience. Write complete sentences for your answer.

Personal Response Would you have joined the Patriots, or would you have remained loyal to the king? Explain your answer.

_____

_____

_____

_____

_____

. . . If You Lived at the Time of the American Revolution (continued)

Grammar, Usage, and Mechanics

Read each question. Fill in the bubble beside the answer in each group that is correct. If none of the answers is correct, choose the last answer, "none of the above."

1. Which sentence contains a comparative adjective?

  Ⓐ Those men are the ones he told you about yesterday.

  Ⓑ Riga and Olga have both just turned twenty years old.

  Ⓒ The dinosaur skeleton was taller than us.

  Ⓓ none of the above

2. Which sentence contains an adjective that tells *how many?*

  Ⓐ My brother had eight candles on his birthday cake.

  Ⓑ The rainbow made colorful patterns in the clouds.

  Ⓒ That paintbrush is the best one to use on the trim.

  Ⓓ none of the above

3. Which sentence contains an adjective that tells *which kind?*

  Ⓐ Snow White lived with the seven dwarves.

  Ⓑ These pears are yellow, while the others are green.

  Ⓒ The tired hikers rested for a while.

  Ⓓ none of the above

4. In which sentence does the adverb modify a verb?

  Ⓐ Jenna felt slightly tired.   Ⓒ The glass was almost empty.

  Ⓑ The spy walked carefully.   Ⓓ none of the above

5. In which sentence does the adverb modify an adjective?

  Ⓐ When coach spoke the team listened closely.

  Ⓑ The captain shouted loudly.

  Ⓒ Last summer, the South had unusually dry weather.

  Ⓓ none of the above

. . . If You Lived at the Time of the American Revolution (continued)

Analyzing the Selection

Read the questions below. Write complete sentences for your answer. Support your answer with information from the selection.

How do you think the American people felt during the Revolutionary War? Keep in mind that most people had little news of the fighting and did not know how the war was going. Do you think that everyday life continued more or less normally?

_____

_____

_____

_____

_____

_____

_____

_____

_____

_____

_____

_____

. . . If You Lived at the Time of the American Revolution (continued)

Oral Fluency Assessment

Golf: A Silly Game?

The bus came to a stop in the parking lot of the golf course.	1–14
A group of students got off and walked to the meeting area.	15–26
Carla Morgan, their teacher's sister, was standing there	27–34
with a few golfers. The children lined up quietly and stared	35–45
at the group of golfers. Among them was Hoop Landers, a	46–56
professional basketball player they all had seen on television.	57–65
Carla introduced all of the players. Then she divided up the	66–76
children into small groups. Alice, Steven, Edward, and two	77–85
others quickly ran over to be with Hoop. He was about to start	86–98
teaching when Steven spoke up.	99–103
"Mr. Landers, how come you're here? Do you like golf? Isn't	104–114
it a silly game compared to basketball or football?"	115–123
Hoop looked at Steven's name tag. Then he said, "Steven,	124–133
there's no such thing as a silly game if you have the right	134–146
attitude. I love basketball, but I started playing golf a few years	147–158
ago so I could spend time with my parents. Here, give it a try."	159–172
The children followed Hoop's directions. Pretty soon they	173–180
were all making good swings. Steven was surprised to see that	181–191
Alice could hit the ball at least as far as he could. He could	192–205
not help but think that maybe golf was not such a silly game	206–218
after all.	219–220

**EVALUATING CODES
FOR ORAL FLUENCY**

sky   (/) words read incorrectly

blue
 ^   sky   (^) inserted word
             ( ]) after the last word

READING RATE AND ACCURACY

Total Words Read: _____

Number of Errors: _____

Number of Correct Words
Read Per Minute (WPM):   _____

Accuracy Rate: _____

(Number of Correct Words Read per
Minute ÷ Total Words Read)

READING FLUENCY

	Low	Average	High
Decoding ability	○	○	○
Pace	○	○	○
Syntax	○	○	○
Self-correction	○	○	○
Intonation	○	○	○

Record student rates on the Oral Fluency Scores pages.

Name _____ Date _____ Score _____

The Midnight Ride of Paul Revere

Vocabulary

Read each item. Fill in the bubble for the answer you think is correct.

1. A **gleam** is a

   Ⓐ small mountain.   Ⓒ horse.

   Ⓑ battleship.   Ⓓ flash of light.

2. What is the meaning of the suffix *-less?*

   Ⓐ action or process   Ⓒ one who does

   Ⓑ without   Ⓓ state of

3. He held the lantern **aloft.** That means he held it

   Ⓐ with both hands.

   Ⓑ near the ground.

   Ⓒ behind his back.

   Ⓓ high above the ground.

4. Paul Revere rode on a **ledge.** A **ledge** is

   Ⓐ a narrow surface.

   Ⓑ a covered wagon.

   Ⓒ a special kind of saddle.

   Ⓓ a large breed of horse.

5. Paul Revere **spread** the word about the British. In this sentence, **spread** means to

   Ⓐ make something known.

   Ⓑ guide someone.

   Ⓒ create something new.

   Ⓓ give shelter to someone.

The Midnight Ride of Paul Revere (continued)

Comprehension

Read the following questions carefully. Then completely fill in the bubble of each correct answer. You may look back at the selection to find the answer to each of the questions.

1. "The Midnight Ride of Paul Revere" was written from the third-person point of view of someone who

    (A) was sent to warn the militia that the British were coming.

    (B) was reporting the event for a newspaper.

    (C) was a British soldier.

    (D) was alive a long time after the event occurred.

2. When did Revere ride?

    (A) April 18, 1875

    (B) after the battle of Lexington and Concord

    (C) April 18, 1775

    (D) after the Declaration of Independence was signed

The Midnight Ride of Paul Revere (continued)

3. Which of these was NOT something Revere did?

  (A) He signed the Declaration of Independence.

  (B) He helped plan the Boston Tea Party.

  (C) He spied on British troop movement around Boston.

  (D) He carried news to and from the Continental Congress.

4. What does Revere's friend see as he first looks down from the church tower?

  (A) the bay

  (B) British troops

  (C) a graveyard

  (D) two lanterns

5. Where did the first battle of the Revolution actually take place?

  (A) Boston

  (B) Lexington

  (C) New York City

  (D) Concord

The Midnight Ride of Paul Revere (continued)

Read the following questions carefully. Use complete sentences to answer the questions. Possible answers below

6. What is Revere's friend doing near the barracks door?

The friend is spying on the British soldiers.

7. What is the difference between what the poem and the historical note say about where the signal lanterns were hung?

The poem says the Old North Church. The note says Christ Church.

8. Why did the British think they would have an easy time defeating the militia in Concord?

They expected a small group, not the over three hundred patriots there.

9. What is the difference between what happened to Revere in the poem and in the historical note?

In the poem, Revere gets to Concord. The note says that he never got there.

10. What happened after the fighting stopped in Lexington?

After it stopped, eight patriots had been killed and the British marched to Concord.

The Midnight Ride of Paul Revere (continued)

Read the question below. Write complete sentences for your answer. Support your answer with information from the selection.

Linking to the Concepts Why was spreading the news about the British so important?

_____

_____

_____

_____

_____

Read the prompt below. Your response should be based on your own experience. Write complete sentences for your response.

Personal Response Think about what Paul Revere did. Write about something you did that was part of a bigger event involving other people.

_____

_____

_____

_____

_____

The Midnight Ride of Paul Revere (continued)

Grammar, Usage, and Mechanics

Read each question. Fill in the bubble beside the answer in each group that is correct. If none of the answers is correct, choose the last answer, "none of the above."

1. In which sentence is a preposition underlined?

   Ⓐ Put it on the <u>table</u>.   Ⓒ <u>Put</u> it on the table.

   Ⓑ Put it <u>on</u> the table.   Ⓓ none of the above

2. In which sentence is a prepositional phrase underlined?

   Ⓐ The sea lion <u>in the tank</u> is part of the show.

   Ⓑ The sea lion in the tank <u>is part</u> of the show.

   Ⓒ The <u>sea lion in</u> the tank is part of the show.

   Ⓓ none of the above

3. In which sentence is the object of the preposition underlined?

   Ⓐ Dayton painted a picture early <u>in</u> the morning.

   Ⓑ Dayton painted a picture <u>early</u> in the morning.

   Ⓒ Dayton painted a picture early in the <u>morning</u>.

   Ⓓ none of the above

4. Which sentence contains a prepositional phrase?

   Ⓐ My brother does not like thunder and lightning.

   Ⓑ Paul wondered how electricity works.

   Ⓒ Ben Franklin flew a kite when it stormed.

   Ⓓ none of the above

5. In this sentence, which word is modified by a prepositional phrase?

   The boys in their tiny red caps ran in the woods.

   Ⓐ tiny   Ⓒ caps

   Ⓑ red   Ⓓ none of the above

The Midnight Ride of Paul Revere (continued)

Analyzing the Selection

Read the questions below. Write complete sentences for your answer. Support your answer with information from the selection.

What are the most important differences between the poem "The Midnight Ride of Paul Revere" and what actually happened? Why do you think Longfellow changed the actual story?

_____

_____

_____

_____

_____

_____

_____

_____

_____

_____

_____

_____

_____

_____

The Midnight Ride of Paul Revere (continued)

Oral Fluency Assessment

Gertrude Ederle

Thousands of people cross between France and England every day. They take planes, ferries, and even trains. An American athlete, Gertrude Ederle, used a different method. She was the first woman to swim across the English Channel.

Ederle was born in New York City in 1906. She started swimming at an early age. Soon she was on her way to becoming one of the most famous swimmers of her time. When she was sixteen, Ederle broke seven records in one day at a meet. Two years later, in 1924, she swam in the Olympics. She won a gold medal in the 400-meter freestyle relay.

After the Olympics, she looked for an even greater test. One of the hardest swims in the world is the twenty-one mile English Channel. The seas in the channel can be rough. The water is cold. In the past, only male swimmers had made the swim.

Most people believed the swim was too difficult for a woman. Ederle wanted to prove them wrong. She did not make it on her first attempt. In 1926, she tried again.

She started from France. Ederle had to swim farther than planned because of heavy seas. She went an extra distance. She still managed to beat the world record by almost two hours. This feat made her famous at the age of twenty.

1–8
9–18
19–26
27–37
38–48
49–60
61–71
72–83
84–95
96–105
106–116
117–129
130–141
142–152
153–162
163–173
174–183
184–193
194–204
205–215
216–225

EVALUATING CODES FOR ORAL FLUENCY

sky (/) words read incorrectly

blue
^ sky (^) inserted word
      ( ]) after the last word

READING RATE AND ACCURACY

Total Words Read: _____

Number of Errors: _____

Number of Correct Words Read Per Minute (WPM): _____

Accuracy Rate: _____

(Number of Correct Words Read per Minute ÷ Total Words Read)

READING FLUENCY

	Low	Average	High
Decoding ability	○	○	○
Pace	○	○	○
Syntax	○	○	○
Self-correction	○	○	○
Intonation	○	○	○

Record student rates on the Oral Fluency Scores pages.

Name _____ Date _____ Score _____

The Master Spy of Yorktown

Vocabulary

Read each item. Fill in the bubble for the answer you think is correct.

1. The base word in **commander** is

Ⓐ command.　　Ⓒ man.

Ⓑ er.　　Ⓓ com.

2. Idle means the same as

Ⓐ a little late.　　Ⓒ not busy.

Ⓑ very fast.　　Ⓓ perfect.

3. According to Thomas Jefferson, Virginia was a state of "mild laws and a people not used to **prompt** obedience." This means that the people

Ⓐ paid their taxes on time every year.

Ⓑ were not quick to follow orders.

Ⓒ did not own much land.

Ⓓ worked hard to make a living.

4. The British were **looting** and burning their way through Virginia. This means that the British were

Ⓐ learning how to herd sheep.

Ⓑ stealing valuable things.

Ⓒ growing crops.

Ⓓ riding a train.

5. Lafayette tried to keep up the morale of Virginia **civilians. Civilians** are

Ⓐ people who are not in the military.　　Ⓒ students.

Ⓑ tobacco farmers.　　Ⓓ traveling preachers.

The Master Spy of Yorktown (continued)

Comprehension

Read the following questions carefully. Then completely fill in the bubble of each correct answer. You may look back at the selection to find the answer to each of the questions.

1. Which of these is a fact about the Marquis de Lafayette?

   Ⓐ He was from France.

   Ⓑ He was a good commander.

   Ⓒ He was very intelligent.

   Ⓓ He was excited to be asked to command an army.

2. Why was Lafayette having a difficult time in Virginia?

   Ⓐ He could not find the British army.

   Ⓑ His army was so large that it was difficult to keep everyone informed.

   Ⓒ The people living there were not very helpful

   Ⓓ He did not have enough American money.

The Master Spy of Yorktown (continued)

3. Who was James Armistead?

 Ⓐ a British commander

 Ⓑ a naval hero

 Ⓒ an American spy

 Ⓓ a French nobleman

4. What happened after Cornwallis's army arrived in Portsmouth?

 Ⓐ The soldiers built defenses immediately.

 Ⓑ General Arnold was almost captured by a band of Virginia soldiers.

 Ⓒ Armistead became a trusted servant of Cornwallis.

 Ⓓ A fleet of ships came to anchor in the harbor.

5. Why did Cornwallis surrender?

 Ⓐ He and his army were surrounded.

 Ⓑ Most of his men were dead.

 Ⓒ He and his army ran out of supplies.

 Ⓓ Most of his men were ill.

The Master Spy of Yorktown (continued)

Read the following questions carefully. Use complete sentences to answer the questions. Possible answers below

6. Why was Lafayette excited about commanding an American force?

He was excited because it was his dream to lead an American army.

7. Why was General Cornwallis so careful with his papers?

He was careful to be sure that enemies could not learn of his plans.

8. Why was Cornwallis surprised to see Armistead in an American uniform?

He was surprised because he had never suspected Armistead was a spy.

9. Why did James Armistead change his name to Lafayette?

He changed it when he became free in honor of the Marquis de Lafayette.

10. How was Saul Matthews like James Armistead?

Both were spies. Both were slaves but became free eventually.

The Master Spy of Yorktown (continued)

Read the question below. Write complete sentences for your answer. Support your answer with information from the selection.

Linking to the Concepts What type of person do you think Armistead was? Use information from the selection and your own opinion.

_____

_____

_____

_____

_____

Read the questions below. Your answer should be based on your own experience. Write complete sentences for your answer.

Personal Response If you had been Armistead, would you have done the things he did? Why or why not?

_____

_____

_____

_____

_____

The Master Spy of Yorktown (continued)

Grammar, Usage, and Mechanics

Read each question. Fill in the bubble beside the answer in each group that is correct. If none of the answers is correct, choose the last answer, "none of the above."

1. Which computer command would you use to remove a word from a document?

  Ⓐ cut   Ⓒ select

  Ⓑ paste   Ⓓ none of the above

2. Before you copy a word, what must you do?

  Ⓐ delete the word

  Ⓑ close the document

  Ⓒ select the word

  Ⓓ none of the above

3. When you move a word from one place to another in a document, what is it called?

  Ⓐ move or not

  Ⓑ try to change

  Ⓒ cut and paste

  Ⓓ none of the above

4. When you have finished working on a document you would like to use in the future, what should you do?

  Ⓐ delete it   Ⓒ explain it

  Ⓑ save it   Ⓓ none of the above

5. What is it called when you use the cursor to identify some words in a document?

  Ⓐ exchanging   Ⓒ highlighting

  Ⓑ replacing   Ⓓ none of the above

The Master Spy of Yorktown (continued)

Analyzing the Selection

Read the questions below. Write complete sentences for your answer. Support your answer with information from the selections.

Think about Armistead and the other people you read about in this unit. What did they think about the future of the new country? Do you think they had high hopes, or were they unsure? Use information from the selection and your own opinions.

_____

_____

_____

_____

_____

_____

_____

_____

_____

_____

_____

_____

_____

_____

The Master Spy of Yorktown (continued)

Oral Fluency Assessment

Eddie and Gramps

Eddie's grandfather did not live in a regular house. He
needed special nursing care. Eddie was sad that his grandfather
could not stay with his family in their house. His mom and dad
said that they could not give him the help that he needed. Eddie
understood, but he did not like it.

The place where Eddie's grandfather lived was called "Elder
Care Nursing Home." It was not an elegant place, but it was
home to a lot of nice people. Eddie tried to visit his grandfather
as often as he could. They had a great relationship. Sometimes
they would play checkers or cards. Mostly, though, they would
just talk.

Eddie was a quiet boy. He usually kept to himself. He spoke
very softly. His grandfather was his best friend. They both
enjoyed each other's company.

Eddie's grandfather—"Gramps" as Eddie called him—had
lived a very exciting life. It was amazing to hear of all the
things he had done. Among other things, he had been a soldier
in the army, a firefighter, and a mason. His stories were always
great. They made Eddie think. When Gramps started telling
stories of his past, Eddie realized that he was lucky to have him
in his life.

1–10
11–20
21–33
34–46
47–53
54–62
63–74
75–87
88–98
99–108
109–110
111–122
123–132
133–136
137–144
145–157
158–169
170–181
182–190
191–203
204–206

**EVALUATING CODES
FOR ORAL FLUENCY**

sky   (/) words read incorrectly

blue
^   sky   (^) inserted word
           ( ]) after the last word

READING RATE AND ACCURACY

Total Words Read: _____

Number of Errors: _____

Number of Correct Words
Read Per Minute (WPM):   _____

Accuracy Rate: _____

(Number of Correct Words Read per
Minute ÷ Total Words Read)

READING FLUENCY

	Low	Average	High
Decoding ability	O	O	O
Pace	O	O	O
Syntax	O	O	O
Self-correction	O	O	O
Intonation	O	O	O

Record student rates on the Oral Fluency Scores pages.

Name _____ Date _____ Score _____

Shh! We're Writing the Constitution

Vocabulary

Read each item. Fill in the bubble for the answer you think is correct.

1. What does the prefix **con-** mean?

   Ⓐ before   Ⓒ too much

   Ⓑ change from   Ⓓ with

2. An **accomplishment** is an

   Ⓐ observation.   Ⓒ illness.

   Ⓑ achievement.   Ⓓ escape.

3. George Washington wanted his troops to swear **allegiance** to the United States. In this sentence, **allegiance** means

   Ⓐ faithful support.

   Ⓑ lasting glory.

   Ⓒ money and funds.

   Ⓓ extra time.

4. Washington hoped to see the states united under one **central** government. In this sentence, **central** means

   Ⓐ elected.   Ⓒ hard-working.

   Ⓑ main.   Ⓓ caring.

5. Each state legislature sent **delegates** to the Continental Congress. **Delegates** are

   Ⓐ people chosen to act for others.

   Ⓑ extra supplies.

   Ⓒ tax money.

   Ⓓ copies of the state's laws.

Shh! We're Writing the Constitution (continued)

Comprehension

Read the following questions carefully. Then completely fill in the bubble of each correct answer. You may look back at the selection to find the answer to each of the questions.

1. Why did the First Continental Congress meet?

    Ⓐ The country needed some type of government.

    Ⓑ The states were concerned about British rule.

    Ⓒ The states badly wanted a strong national government.

    Ⓓ The states needed to raise taxes.

2. Which of these was NOT a reason delegates gave for being late to the convention?

    Ⓐ They did not have enough money.

    Ⓑ The roads were muddy.

    Ⓒ They had personal business to attend to.

    Ⓓ The British Army was advancing.

Shh! We're Writing the Constitution (continued)

3. Which of these is an opinion about James Madison?

Ⓐ Madison arrived in Philadelphia eleven days early.

Ⓑ Madison sat in the front of the room.

Ⓒ Madison was worked up about the meeting.

Ⓓ Madison was never absent for a session.

4. Which of these is a fact about Edmund Randolph?

Ⓐ Randolph was the governor of Virginia.

Ⓑ Randolph was likable.

Ⓒ Randolph was handsome.

Ⓓ Randolph did not say alarming things.

5. The author wrote this piece in order to

Ⓐ explain the Constitution to the readers.

Ⓑ convince readers that Thomas Jefferson was a great writer.

Ⓒ tell about how the Constitution came to be.

Ⓓ show that early Americans did not trust people from other states.

Shh! We're Writing the Constitution (continued)

Read the following questions carefully. Use complete sentences to answer the questions. Possible answers below

6. After the Revolutionary War, why were most people in America not ready to call themselves Americans?

The people felt they were citizens of their states first.

7. What was the first thing the convention delegates did?

They elected George Washington president of the convention.

8. Why were the windows of the meeting house kept closed although it was hot outside?

They were kept closed so no one could listen in on the sessions.

9. What was the Virginia Plan?

It was Randolph's model of what the national government would be.

10. What was Alexander Hamilton's opinion about the president's term of office?

He favored a long term to prevent having a lot of ex-presidents around.

Shh! We're Writing the Constitution (continued)

Read the question below. Write complete sentences for your answer. Support your answer with information from the selection.

Linking to the Concepts What might have happened had the states remained "sovereign"?

_____

_____

_____

_____

Read the questions below. Your answer should be based on your own experience. Write complete sentences for your answer.

Personal Response How would you have felt if you were helping to write the Constitution? Would you be able to work easily with the other people?

_____

_____

_____

_____

Shh! We're Writing the Constitution (continued)

Grammar, Usage, and Mechanics

Read each question. Fill in the bubble beside the answer in each group that is correct. If none of the answers is correct, choose the last answer, "none of the above."

1. Which sentence has correct capitalization?

Ⓐ Raul writes for *Popular Mechanics* magazine.

Ⓑ Raul writes for *Popular mechanics* magazine.

Ⓒ raul writes for *popular mechanics* magazine.

Ⓓ none of the above

2. Which sentence has a mistake in capitalization?

Ⓐ Have you seen *Bambi* on DVD?

Ⓑ Gary Paulsen is the author of *Hatchet*.

Ⓒ The House of Representatives is in session now.

Ⓓ none of the above

3. Which item has correct capitalization?

Ⓐ Winter in Palm Beach, Florida

Ⓒ winter in Palm Beach, Florida

Ⓑ Winter in palm Beach, Florida

Ⓓ none of the above

4. Which sentence has correct capitalization?

Ⓐ Driving through south Dakota, we saw many farms.

Ⓑ People visit new York to see the Statue of Liberty.

Ⓒ The airline has a new price for trips to europe.

Ⓓ none of the above

5. Which sentence has a mistake in capitalization?

Ⓐ Uncle ned took his nephews to a beach in Maryland.

Ⓑ The plane stopped in Poland, Denmark, and Greenland.

Ⓒ Dr. Liu came here from Asia about ten years ago.

Ⓓ none of the above

Shh! We're Writing the Constitution (continued)

Analyzing the Selection

Read the questions below. Write complete sentences for your answer. Support your answer with information from the selection.

Not many people know how difficult it was to write the Constitution. What were some of the challenges that the delegates faced, and how did they resolve them? What did you find most surprising about the process?

_____

_____

_____

_____

_____

_____

_____

_____

_____

_____

_____

_____

Shh! We're Writing the Constitution (continued)

Oral Fluency Assessment

Cathy Is a Big Help

Michael did not know much about cars, especially how they	1–10
are constructed. That is why Cathy suggested that she help him.	11–21
Cathy grew up working with her father. Her family's garage	22–31
was like a workshop and her father was always building or	32–42
fixing something. Cathy was right beside him, helping him out	43–52
whether he liked it or not. He made cabinets and shelves for	53–64
her mother and built a dollhouse for Cathy. And her father was	65–76
always working on his classic car.	77–82
Cathy got pretty good with tools and knowing how things	83–92
work, especially with cars. She liked to think that her dad's	93–103
car would have never been wheeled out of the garage without	104–114
her help.	115–116
The big race was called "The Little Grand Prix of	117–126
Clintonville." The rules were simple. The entry had to be a	127–137
two-person car made out of wood and metal. It had to have four	138–151
wheels and be powered only by gravity. The race took place	152–162
down a hill.	163–165
Cathy had run into Michael while walking to the store.	166–175
"Come on, Michael," Cathy said. "You and I could build the	176–186
best car out there."	187–190
On the way back, Cathy was very excited about the	191–200
whole thing and thought that she and Michael would make a	201–211
wonderful, and winning, team.	212–215

EVALUATING CODES FOR ORAL FLUENCY

sky   (/) words read incorrectly

blue

^ sky   (^) inserted word

( ]) after the last word

READING RATE AND ACCURACY

Total Words Read: _____

Number of Errors: _____

Number of Correct Words
Read Per Minute (WPM): _____

Accuracy Rate: _____

(Number of Correct Words Read per
Minute ÷ Total Words Read)

READING FLUENCY

	Low	Average	High
Decoding ability	○	○	○
Pace	○	○	○
Syntax	○	○	○
Self-correction	○	○	○
Intonation	○	○	○

Record student rates on the Oral Fluency Scores pages.

Name _____ **Date** _____ **Score** _____

Give Me Liberty!

Vocabulary

Read each item. Fill in the bubble for the answer you think is correct.

1. A **declaration** is a type of

 Ⓐ question.   Ⓒ honor.

 Ⓑ concern.   Ⓓ statement.

2. What is the superlative form of the adjective **good?**

 Ⓐ betterest   Ⓒ better

 Ⓑ best   Ⓓ goodest

3. British warships **bombarded** the seaport of Charleston, South Carolina. In this sentence, **bombarded** means

 Ⓐ attacked with heavy fire. Ⓒ crowded inside.

 Ⓑ surrounded completely. Ⓓ steered clear of.

4. Congress held its final **debate** on the idea of independence. A **debate** is a(n)

 Ⓐ election between two or more candidates.

 Ⓑ rough draft of a written document.

 Ⓒ discussion between groups that disagree.

 Ⓓ open trial with a judge and a jury.

5. People worried that seeking independence would be like **exposing** a new family before they found another shelter. In this sentence, **exposing** means

 Ⓐ trying to prove something is right.

 Ⓑ leaving something unprotected.

 Ⓒ looking for something that does not exist.

 Ⓓ giving up something for the benefit of all.

Give Me Liberty! (continued)

Comprehension

Read the following questions carefully. Then completely fill in the bubble of each correct answer. You may look back at the selection to find the answer to each of the questions.

1. What happened right after the final version of the Declaration of Independence was voted on and approved unanimously?

   (A) Copies were carried by express to the villages.

   (B) A boy at the door gave a signal for bells to ring.

   (C) All members of Congress signed the form.

   (D) A copy was sent by ship to King George.

2. The statement "The delegates who favored independence got busy behind the scenes" suggests that they

   (A) worked together to persuade the other delegates.

   (B) helped Jefferson with his draft of the declaration.

   (C) asked Adams to give a speech.

   (D) leaked negative information to the newspapers.

Give Me Liberty! (continued)

3. The author says that Jefferson "squirmed in his seat" while Congress worked on his draft. This phrase suggests that Jefferson was

   Ⓐ bored with the meeting.

   Ⓑ shy about what he had written.

   Ⓒ uncomfortable with the process.

   Ⓓ eager to get to another appointment.

4. What made the delegates want to vote quickly on July 4th?

   Ⓐ The summer heat was unbearable.

   Ⓑ The colonies were demanding freedom.

   Ⓒ The assembly room was filled with horseflies.

   Ⓓ The noise outside the statehouse door was distracting.

5. At this point in his career, Jefferson was all of the following EXCEPT

   Ⓐ a scholar.

   Ⓑ a writer.

   Ⓒ a delegate.

   Ⓓ a president.

Give Me Liberty! (continued)

Read the following questions carefully. Use complete sentences to answer the questions. Possible answers below

6. What are some of the reasons Adams believed Jefferson was the better man to draft the Declaration of Independence?

Jefferson was a Virginian, popular, and a better writer than Adams.

7. According to the selection, what sources did Jefferson draw upon while writing his draft?

He drew upon the writings of Locke and Paine, and other declarations.

8. What did the delegates risk by signing the Declaration of Independence?

The delegates risked being captured and killed as traitors by the British.

9. Why did John Hancock make his signature so large?

He wanted it to be big enough for King George to read without his glasses.

10. What did Jefferson state was the purpose of the Declaration of Independence?

The purpose was to explain that all people are created equal and they have rights.

Give Me Liberty! (continued)

Read the question below. Write complete sentences for your answer. Support your answer with information from the selection.

Linking to the Concepts How are the ideas of equality and the rights to life, liberty and the pursuit of happiness still important today?

_____

_____

_____

_____

_____

Read the question below. Your answer should be based on your own experience. Write complete sentences for your answer.

Personal Response Imagine you were Thomas Jefferson. How would you have responded to the edits or comments about the draft you had written?

_____

_____

_____

_____

_____

_____

Give Me Liberty! (continued)

Grammar, Usage, and Mechanics

Read each question. Fill in the bubble beside the answer in each group that is correct. If none of the answers is correct, choose the last answer, "none of the above."

1. In which sentence is the adverb used correctly?

Ⓐ On our team, Pat moves more quicker than Len.

Ⓑ On our team, Pat moves quicker than Len.

Ⓒ On our team, Pat quicker most moves than Len.

Ⓓ none of the above

2. In which sentence is the adjective used correctly?

Ⓐ Tyrone won a prize for the liveliest presentation.

Ⓑ Tyrone won a prize for the most liveliest presentation.

Ⓒ Tyrone won a prize for the most livelier presentation.

Ⓓ none of the above

3. In which sentence is a preposition underlined?

Ⓐ Everyone in the talent <u>show</u> gets a turn on the stage.

Ⓑ <u>Everyone</u> in the talent show gets a turn on the stage.

Ⓒ Everyone in the talent show gets a turn <u>on</u> the stage.

Ⓓ none of the above

4. In which sentence is a prepositional phrase underlined?

Ⓐ A tiger's striped coat lets it blend <u>into the forest</u>.

Ⓑ A tiger's <u>striped coat</u> lets it blend into the forest.

Ⓒ A tiger's striped coat <u>lets it blend</u> into the forest.

Ⓓ none of the above

5. What would you use to move text in a document?

Ⓐ spell-check

Ⓑ cut and paste

Ⓒ save

Ⓓ none of the above

Give Me Liberty! (continued)

Analyzing the Selection

Read the questions below. Write complete sentences for your answer. Support your answer with information from the selections.

More than anything else, the American Revolution was successful because the people involved were motivated to make a new country. Why were they so driven? What made them willing to take on the strongest country in the world at the time? Use information from the selections as well as your opinion and prior knowledge.

_____

_____

_____

_____

_____

_____

_____

_____

_____

_____

_____

_____

_____

_____

_____

Give Me Liberty! (continued)

Oral Fluency Assessment

Silk

Many years ago, the Chinese discovered a secret. Boiling the	1–10
cocoons of a type of caterpillar called a silkworm gave them	11–21
long, unbroken threads. When this thread was woven, the cloth	22–31
was soft and shiny. They called it silk.	32–39
At first they gathered the cocoons in the wild. This wild silk	40–51
often had holes in it or tiny marks. Later they began raising	52–63
the worms on their own farms. If these silkworms were kept in	64–75
special trays, the thread would be unmarked.	76–82
Taking care of silkworms was not easy. Before they spin	83–92
their cocoons, silkworms eat constantly. A village worked	93–100
day and night to gather enough mulberry leaves to feed the	101–111
silkworms. Cocoons had to be boiled. If they did not boil them,	112–123
the moths poked holes in them. All this work made silk costly.	124–135
Because it was tightly woven, soldiers realized silk could	136–144
stop arrows. They wore silk under their armor. During World	145–154
War I, silk was used to make bulletproof vests. Parachutes and	155–165
tires can also be made of silk. Chinese doctors even used silk	166–177
to make new veins for people. Though it is soft and beautiful,	178–189
silk is also strong, so it is used for many things besides	190–201
fancy clothing.	202–203

EVALUATING CODES FOR ORAL FLUENCY

sky   (/) words read incorrectly

blue
^   sky   (^) inserted word
           ( ]) after the last word

READING RATE AND ACCURACY

Total Words Read: _____

Number of Errors: _____

Number of Correct Words
Read Per Minute (WPM):   _____

Accuracy Rate: _____

(Number of Correct Words Read per
Minute ÷ Total Words Read)

READING FLUENCY

	Low	Average	High
Decoding ability	○	○	○
Pace	○	○	○
Syntax	○	○	○
Self-correction	○	○	○
Intonation	○	○	○

Record student rates on the Oral Fluency Scores pages.

Name _____ **Date** _____ **Score** _____

Persuasive Writing

Writing Situation
The most important event in early American history

Audience
Your classmates

Directions for Writing
Many important events happened around the time of the American Revolution. Which one do you think was most important? Describe the event and explain why you think it was important. Write in a way that will convince the reader that your opinion is sound.

Checklist
You will earn the best score if you
- choose an event you know well and think is important.
- plan your writing before you begin.
- state your point of view clearly in the first paragraph.
- include facts or examples that support your point of view.
- mention the historic event several times.
- use words that tell how you feel about the event.
- explain the event clearly to your readers.
- avoid words and phrases that are often overused.
- vary your sentences and the words you use.
- choose words that are strong, colorful, and accurately express your ideas.

UNIT 3 — Four Point Rubrics for Persuasive Writing

Genre	1 Point	2 Points	3 Points	4 Points
Persuasive	Position is absent or confusing. Insufficient writing to show that criteria are met.	Position is vague or lacks clarity. Unrelated ideas or multiple positions are included.	An opening statement identifies position. Writing may develop few or more points than delineated in opening. Focus may be too broad.	Sets scope and purpose of paper in introduction. Maintains position throughout. Supports arguments. Includes effective closing.
Writing Traits				
Audience	Displays little or no sense of audience. Does not engage audience.	Displays some sense of audience.	Writes with audience in mind throughout.	Displays a strong sense of audience. Engages audience.
Focus	Topic is unclear or wanders and must be inferred. Extraneous material may be present.	Topic/position/direction is unclear and must be inferred.	Topic/position is stated and direction/purpose is previewed and maintained. Mainly stays on topic.	Topic/position is clearly stated, previewed, and maintained throughout the paper. Topics and details are tied together with a central theme or purpose that is maintained /threaded throughout the paper.
Organization	The writing lacks coherence; organization seems haphazard and disjointed. Plan is not evident. Facts are presented randomly. No transitions are included. Beginning is weak and ending is abrupt. There is no awareness of paragraph structure or organization.	An attempt has been made to organize the writing; however, the overall structure is inconsistent or skeletal. Plan is evident but loosely structured or writer overuses a particular pattern. Writing may be a listing of facts/ideas with a weak beginning or conclusion. Transitions are awkward or nonexistent. Includes beginning use of paragraphs.	Organization is clear and coherent. Order and structure are present, but may seem formulaic. Plan is evident. Reasons for order of key concepts may be unclear. Beginning or conclusion is included but may lack impact. Transitions are present. Paragraph use is appropriate.	The organization enhances the central idea and its development. The order and structure are compelling and move the reader through the text easily. Plan is evident. Key concepts are logically sequenced. Beginning grabs attention. Conclusion adds impact. Uses a variety of transitions that enhance meaning. Uses paragraphs appropriately.
Writing Conventions				
Conventions Overall	Numerous errors in usage, grammar, spelling, capitalization, and punctuation repeatedly distract the reader and make the text difficult to read. The reader finds it difficult to focus on the message.	The writing demonstrates limited control of standard writing conventions (punctuation, spelling, capitalization, grammar, and usage). Errors sometimes impede readability.	The writing demonstrates control of standard writing conventions (punctuation, spelling, capitalization, grammar, and usage). Minor errors, while perhaps noticeable, do not impede readability.	The writing demonstrates exceptionally strong control of standard writing conventions (punctuation, spelling, capitalization, grammar, and usage) and uses them effectively to enhance communication. Errors are so few and so minor that the reader can easily skim over them.

Six Point Rubrics

Use the following rubrics to assess student writing.

6 Points

The writing is focused, purposeful, and reflects insight into the writing situation. The paper conveys a sense of completeness and wholeness with adherence to the main idea, and its organizational pattern provides for a logical progression of ideas. The support is substantial, specific, relevant, concrete, and/or illustrative. The paper demonstrates a commitment to and an involvement with the subject, clarity in presentation of ideas, and may use creative writing strategies appropriate to the purpose of the paper. The writing demonstrates a mature command of language (word choice) with freshness of expression. Sentence structure is varied, and sentences are complete except when fragments are used purposefully. Few, if any, convention errors occur in mechanics, usage, and punctuation.

5 Points

The writing focuses on the topic, and its organizational pattern provides for a progression of ideas, although some lapses may occur. The paper conveys a sense of completeness or wholeness. The support is ample. The writing demonstrates a mature command of language, including precise word choice. There is variation in sentence structure, and, with rare exceptions, sentences are complete except when fragments are used purposefully. The paper generally follows the conventions of mechanics, usage, and spelling.

4 Points

The writing is generally focused on the topic but may include extraneous or loosely related material. An organizational pattern is apparent, although some lapses may occur. The paper exhibits some sense of completeness or wholeness. The support, including word choice, is adequate, although development may be uneven. There is little variation in sentence structure, and most sentences are complete. The paper generally follows the conventions of mechanics, usage, and spelling.

3 Points

The writing is generally focused on the topic but may include extraneous or loosely related material. An organizational pattern has been attempted, but the paper may lack a sense of completeness or wholeness. Some support is included, but developemt is erratic. Word choice is adequate but may be limited, predictable, or occasionally vague. There is little, if any, variation in sentence structure. Knowledge of the conventions of mechanics and usage is usually demonstrated, and commonly used words are usually spelled correctly.

2 Points

The writing is related to the topic but includes extraneous or loosely related material. Little evidence of an organizational pattern may be demonstrated, and the paper may lack a sense of completeness or wholeness. Development of support is inadequate or illogical. Word choice is limited, inappropriate, or vague. There is little, if any, variation in sentence structure, and gross errors in sentence structure may occur. Errors in basic conventions of mechanics and usage may occur, and commonly used words may be misspelled.

1 Point

The writing may only minimally address the topic. The paper is fragmentary or incoherent listing of related ideas or sentences or both. Little, if any, development of support or an organizational pattern or both is apparent. Limited or inappropriate word choice may obscure meaning. Gross errors in sentence structure and usage may impede communication. Frequent and blatant errors may occur in the basic conventions of mechanics and usage, and commonly used words may be misspelled.

Unscorable

The paper is unscorable because
- the response is not related to what the prompt requested the student to do.
- the response is simply a rewording of the prompt
- the response is a copy of a published work.
- the student refused to write.
- the response is illegible.
- the response is incomprehensible (words are arrange in such a way that no meaning is conveyed).
- the response contains an insufficient amount of writing to determine if the student was attempting to address the prompt.

Oral Fluency Scores

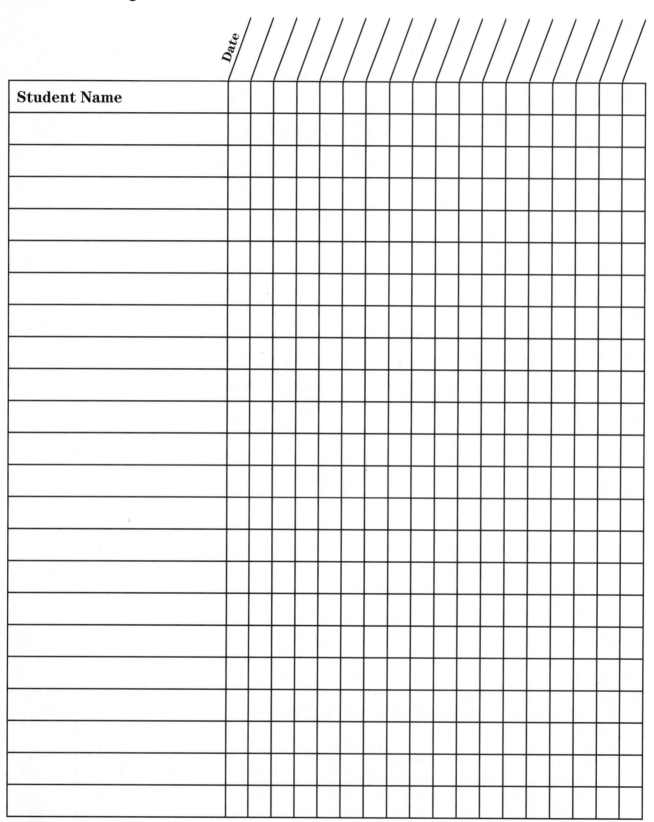

Student Name	Date														

Oral Fluency Scores

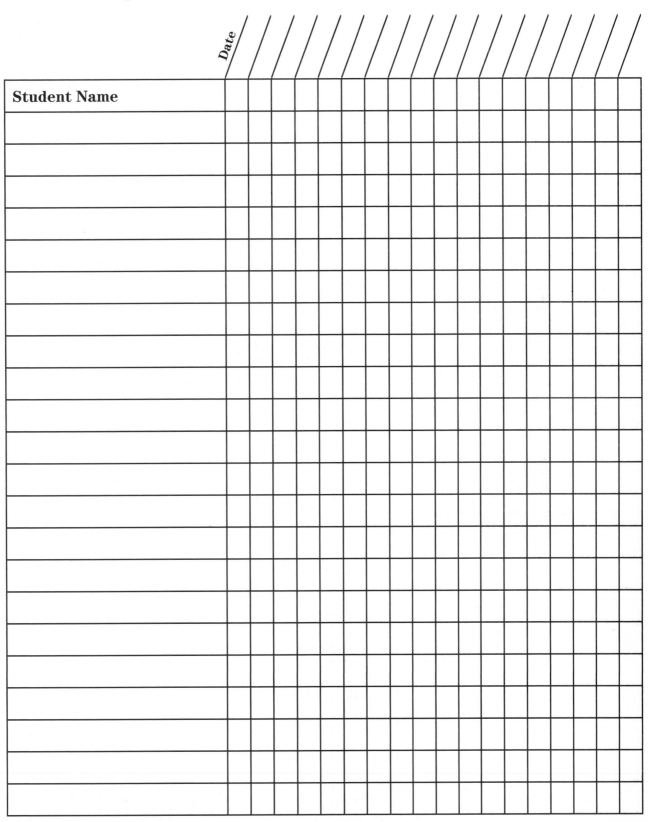

Class Assessment Record

Student Name	Unit 1, Lesson 1	Unit 1, Lesson 2	Unit 1, Lesson 3	Unit 1, Lesson 4	Unit 1, Lesson 5	Unit 1 Writing Prompt	Unit 2, Lesson 1	Unit 2, Lesson 2	Unit 2, Lesson 3

Class Assessment Record

Student Name	Unit 2, Lesson 4	Unit 2, Lesson 5	Unit 2 Writing Prompt	Unit 3, Lesson 1	Unit 3, Lesson 2	Unit 3, Lesson 3	Unit 3, Lesson 4	Unit 3, Lesson 5	Unit 3 Writing Prompt

Student Assessment Record

Name _____

Teacher _____ Grade _____

Unit/ Lesson	Assessment Section	Date	Number Possible	Number Right	%	Score (Rubrics/WPM)

Comprehension Observation Log

Student _____ **Date** _____

Unit _____ **Lesson** _____ **Selection Title** _____

General Comprehension
Concepts discussed: _____

_____

Behavior Within a Group
Articulates, expresses ideas: _____

_____

Joins discussions: _____

_____

Collaborates (such as *works well with other students, works alone*): _____

_____

Role in Group
Role (such as *leader, summarizer, questioner, critic, observer, non-participant*): _____

_____

Flexibility (changes roles when necessary): _____

_____

Use of Reading Strategies
Uses strategies when needed (either those taught or student's choice of strategy)/Describes strategies used:

_____

_____

Changes strategies when appropriate: _____

_____

Changes Since Last Observation
_____
_____
_____